Welcome to…

iPhone
for Beginners

The iPhone is the device that changed the world of mobile phones. No longer were they just a way of making calls or sending texts, now they could be a games console, a task manager, a multimedia player or anything you really want it to be. And as Apple has updated the device, it's just got better and better. But if you're new to the world of iOS, or you're not familiar with everything your handset has to offer, **iPhone for Beginners** is the perfect guide to help you learn about your device. From syncing and setting up to essential apps and FAQs, everything you need to know about your iPhone is included within these 180 pages, so let's get started…

iPhone
for Beginners

Imagine Publishing Ltd
Richmond House
33 Richmond Hill
Bournemouth
Dorset BH2 6EZ
☎ +44 (0) 1202 586200
Website: www.imagine-publishing.co.uk

Editor in Chief
Aaron Asadi

Production Editor
Jon White

Design
Annabelle Sing, Dani Dixon

Photo Studio
Studio equipment courtesy of Lastolite (www.lastolite.co.uk)

Printed by
William Gibbons, 26 Planetary Road, Willenhall, West Midlands, WV13 3XT

Distributed in the UK & Eire by
Imagine Publishing Ltd, www.imagineshop.co.uk. Tel 01202 586200

Distributed in Australia by
Gordon & Gotch, Equinox Centre, 18 Rodborough Road, Frenchs Forest,
NSW 2086. Tel + 61 2 9972 8800

Distributed in the Rest of the World by
Marketforce, Blue Fin Building, 110 Southwark Street, London, SE1 0SU

Contents

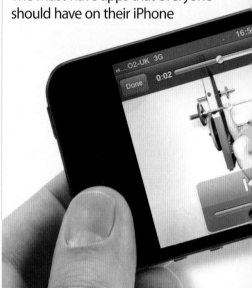

"The Retina display means photos will look better than ever"

Essential apps

Troubleshooting

The next step

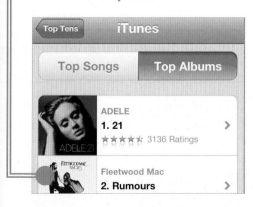

Get to know your iPhone

Exploring the hardware and software of your iPhone

The iPhone is unlike any smartphone you've ever put your hands on. It is the device that changed everything, and opened up a whole new world of possibilities. People who before had no interest in smartphones or mobile computing were becoming experts in the field, eagerly anticipating the latest update or newest release.

When it comes to the iPhone, there's no intermediary between you and what you're trying to do. On a regular desktop computer, you have to learn to manipulate a pointing device like a mouse or trackpad to move a cursor on the screen so you can achieve what you need to do. On the iPhone, you're already an expert manipulator since you just use your fingers directly on the screen to move and affect what you see. If you know how to point, you know how to use an iPhone, and that's the truly exciting thing about this device: it makes personal computing truly personal.

But despite its obvious friendliness, it's still a remarkably complex piece of hardware and you'll need to know a little about what makes the iPhone tick: how you turn it on, for instance, what's the function of its few buttons, and what about all the other controls embedded in the software itself? How can you use its many features to the fullest? Just finding your way around a few basic functions will open up a whole new world of possibilities, and then taking that a step further will allow you to increase your iPhone's practicality and functionality no end.

Throughout these pages we will endeavour to show you all of this, helping you feel comfortable with the device so you can hit the ground running in no time at all. Covering the basics of the hardware, how to get iTunes up and running, some quick tips and tricks to help personalise your device and a complete guide to the functions of your iPhone, this is the perfect place to start learning about your device.

"If you know how to point, then you know how to use an iPhone"

The iPhone home screen explained
Learn your way around

Camera
One touch and you'll be able to snap away!

Message
You can send messages and record conversations from here.

App Store
Access the App Store and download apps from here.

Icons
These little icons represent the apps on your iPhone.

Phone
Call friends and family straight from this app.

Dock
Here you'll find the apps Apple feel you'll use the most.

Explore the iPhone hardware
All the parts you need to know

Wi-Fi signal strength
This symbol lets you know the signal strength it is receiving.

The on/off switch
Turn your iPhone on or off by holding the top-right button.

Volume controls
Use the plus and minus buttons to alter volume levels at any point. There's also a key which can be slid down to mute the iPhone.

Battery level indicator
You can visually see how much power your iPhone has left here.

Screen
The 960x640 Retina display gives a crystal-clear viewing experience.

The Home button
This button takes you back to the iPhone's Home screen.

Speaker grille and microphone
The speaker and microphone are located either side of the connector slot at the base of the iPhone.

The dock connector to sync and/or recharge
This is where you plug in your lead to sync or charge the iPhone to your computer.

TESCO 100% 10:08 Tuesday 24 May

slide to unlock

Browsing

As soon as you've connected to your local wireless network, the iPhone is ready to be an internet browsing device. In fact, when Apple's engineers were first experimenting with touch-screen devices, the original idea was a tablet designed for web browsing. As a result, going online is a very polished experience and a joy to use. Like all other applications on the iPhone, tapping on the Safari icon fills the screen with that program's content, removing any other distractions from view. You can then browse the web with your fingers. If you're familiar with Safari on your Mac or PC, you'll feel right at home – there's even a Google search field, top right of the screen. Tapping on it increases its size and reveals the keyboard so you can type what you're looking for. The same applies for the address field if you know exactly where you want to go. If you're a MobileMe subscriber, you can sync your Mac's bookmarks straight to your iPhone, right down to the Bookmark Bar.

Navigating a webpage is easy; you flick your finger up, down, left or right to see other parts of the page. If you want to focus on a specific section, double-tap on it for it to zoom in and fill the screen.

There are other browsers on the App Store, such as Opera Mini and Atomic, so have a browse to see if one suits your needs better than Safari.

Communication

Browsing the web isn't the only thing you need to do online. For one thing, you need to check your emails and the iPhone's got you covered there as well, thanks to the Mail application. With it, you can set up as many accounts as you need. Just like Mail on your Mac, you have a universal inbox where all your messages, irrespective of which address they were sent to, can be accessed, read and replied to. .

When it comes to social networking, you can either make use of Safari – aside from its games, Facebook works very well in the iPhone's web browser (the games don't work because they rely on Adobe's Flash platform, which isn't compatible with the iPhone, iPad or iPod touch) – or look for dedicated programs available through the App Store. Twitter is a good example of an original design to help you check your timeline easily via your iPhone.

Of course, with all the other functions it would be easy to forget that the iPhone is in essence a phone, so you can call friends and send message till

First steps

Getting acquainted with your iPhone

Turn on
When an iPhone's screen is off, your device is either asleep or shut down…

01. To turn it back on or wake it up, you have two options: you can either press the on/off button, top right of the device…

02. Alternatively, pressing the Home button will also work to bring your iPhone back to life.

Sleep mode
Putting your iPhone to sleep is something you'll find yourself doing quite often.

01. You need to make use of one of your iPhone's few physical buttons for this, namely the one top right of the device.

Turn off
Most of the time, you'll keep the iPhone on, but asleep. To shut down, do the following:

01. Press and hold on its on/off button for up to five seconds. The screen will dim and a red slider will appear.

02. Press and release it once for the screen to go dark and become unresponsive to any touch inputs.

02. Slide that red button from left to right to confirm that you wish to shut the iPhone down.

Change volume

Depending on what you're doing, you can change the volume is various ways...

01. Use the physical buttons, top of the iPhone's left edge. The top one increases the volume and the bottom one lowers it.

02. If you're watching a movie or listening to music, you'll find a slider on the screen to achieve the same result.

Mute

To mute the volume, you have two options based on the iPhone's physical buttons:

01. There's a switch above the volume controls; slide it down to mute.

02. You can also press and hold the volume down button. After a couple of seconds, your iPhone will be muted.

Rotation lock

You may wish to stop the screen from rotating each time you change position. Here's how:

01. Double-tap on the home button to reveal a list of currently running apps. Slide that list to the left.

02. You'll find another volume control, bottom right. The rotation lock button is located bottom left of the screen.

Charging

Recharging the iPhone is a simple matter:

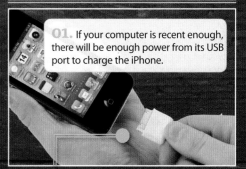

01. If your computer is recent enough, there will be enough power from its USB port to charge the iPhone.

02. For a faster, more efficient charge, it's best to use the bundled power adapter instead.

Brightness

If the screen is too light or dark for your tastes, you can alter it in Settings:

01. Tap on the Settings app and select the 'Brightness & Wallpaper' menu. Use the slider to lower or raise the brightness.

Unlock

Once you've woken your iPhone up, you'll be graced with its Lock Screen. What next?

01. To gain access to your device, use the slider at the bottom to unlock your screen.

02. If you have set a password, you'll have to type it in before you can proceed any further.

Syncing

To back up or transfer files, you need to sync...

01. Use the bundled cable to connect your iPhone via one of your computer's USB ports.

02. It will launch iTunes and the backup and syncing process will be totally automatic.

your heart's content, all with a contract from one of the network providers. FaceTime also allows you to video chat with other compatible devices for free.

Photos

Until the release of the iPad 2, the iPhone had one major selling point over its bigger brother, and that was its front-facing and rear-facing cameras. Of course this the norm in almost every mobile phone you get these days, and although the quality may not be the best on the market, you can download apps to turn your photos into humorous images, and store them in the Photos section of your phone. This virtual photo album makes storing your images quick and painless, and by syncing your device to your computer you can transfer over all your snaps taken on your digital handheld camera.

If you see images on the web you'd like to keep, you can easily save them to your Photos application by tapping and holding on one and choosing 'Save Image' from the popover menu. But that's not the only use of that particular program. Thanks to iTunes on your Mac, you can transfer some or all of your images from your iPhoto or Aperture library straight to your iPhone.

Music

It wouldn't be an Apple device if it didn't let you listen to your music, but although iTunes is responsible for almost everything media-related on your Mac, the iPhone has broken those features into multiple applications designed for specific purposes. For instance, you can purchase new music using the iTunes application, but if you want to listen to albums you currently own, then you have to use the iPod software instead. From there, you gain access to your songs, podcasts and audiobooks. If you want to watch a music video however, you'll need to take a trip to the Videos application.

But iTunes isn't the only way you can listen to music on your iPhone. There are other programs that let you stream songs directly from the internet and just like the iPod application, they can be used to listen to music in the background while you work in another program on your iPhone. If you're in the UK, make sure you check out Spotify, while US readers should take a look at Pandora. There are also a range of radio apps available, but be wary that they can be quite data-intensive if you're on a limited contract.

Watching

Although it's no substitute for your widescreen television, when you're away from your couch the iPhone makes for a surprisingly good TV. Although it's size means it won't be as good as an iPad or MacBook, it will still get the job done. You can play anything you've bought or rented from the iTunes Store and it will work on your iPhone: you can transfer movies, TV shows, podcasts and music videos and they'll play flawlessly on your device.

You could also convert your existing DVD collection into iTunes-compatible files but in order

"Videos all play flawlessly on your portable device"

to achieve this, you'd need programs like HandBrake which are designed to transform your films and episodes into compatible files ready for you to enjoy on your iPhone. This can be a time-consuming process, so if you'd rather not have to deal with any of this and you happen to own an Elgato Netstream device which is connected to your network, you can purchase the EyeTV application and watch live TV straight from your iPhone, anywhere in your house, as long as you're within range of your wireless signal.

Entertainment

There's been a lot of talk about the iPhone (and any other iOS device) not being compatible with Adobe's Flash, but this is actually less of a problem than you might think. For one thing, although you won't be able to go to www.youtube.com and watch videos via the Safari web browser, there's a dedicated YouTube application which enables you to do just that. You can watch clips, comment on them, and do pretty much everything you'd expect. Other video-sharing sites, like Vimeo, are getting on the iOS-friendly bandwagon and offer iPhone-compatible versions of their videos, so you can watch those straight from your web browser. But being entertained is much more than just passively watching something on the screen; you can also use your iPhone to read the latest bestseller or enjoy a timeless classic. The two major programs that allow you to do this are Apple's own iBooks and Amazon's Kindle. Both are also compatible with the iPod and iPad so you can stop reading on

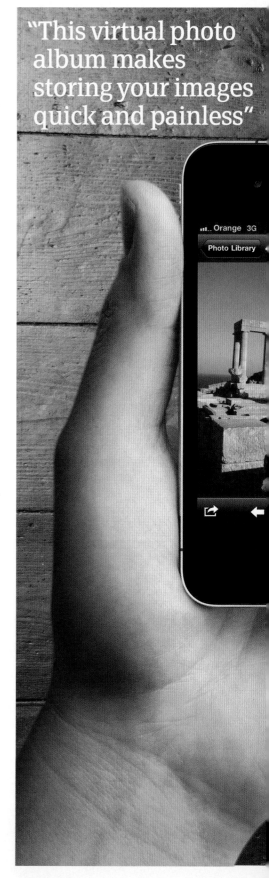

"This virtual photo album makes storing your images quick and painless"

iTunes

The desktop software explored

FAQ

What is iTunes?
A It's a program designed by Apple and the original purpose was to transfer your CD collection onto your Mac, catalogue your songs and transfer them to a compatible MP3 player. A lot's changed since these humble days.

Why do I need it?
A Because iTunes evolved over the years to accommodate more than music – from movies, TV shows, podcasts and more. It's the most popular way to transfer anything to your iPhone.

Why is it not included on a CD?
A Apple now assumes that broadband is ubiquitous and that way, the company can make sure that you'll be using the very latest version available as opposed to one that could have been released months previously.

How do I cancel the sync?
A When your iPhone is connected to iTunes, its screen informs you not to disconnect it from your computer. However, there's a slider at the bottom which you can use to cancel the sync should you need to. Your iPhone will not be fully backed up if you do this, however.

Is there anything else I need to do?
A Not really. The process is completely automatic and if you don't want to get any more involved in the process, you don't have to. Once the sync is complete, you can unplug your device and carry on using it.

Can I control what's on it?
A Absolutely. Look down iTunes' sidebar until you find the Devices section. Click on your iPhone

Where can I get it?
A Point your browser towards **www.itunes.com** and click on the 'Download iTunes' button, somewhere on the page (it's currently on the right, near the top, but that could change).

It's installed. Now what?
A Double-click on its icon to open it and agree to the licence agreement. You can convert your music CDs to iPhone-compatible files or purchase new songs, movies and shows from the iTunes Store. But none of this is compulsory.

What happens when I connect my iPhone to my computer?
A iTunes will take over your iPhone and you will be asked not to disconnect it while the syncing process is taking place. Your iPhone's data will be backed up and your media will be synchronised between both devices.

and the main part of the interface will let you choose which songs, films, podcasts, applications and so on you'd like to transfer over.

What about my emails, calendars and contacts?
A That's all possible as well from the same section in iTunes as mentioned above. You can find all the details and choose which calendars, contacts and emails you'd like to import from the Info section.

Hardware

Clear
The iPhone's Retina display makes viewing the web a pixel-perfect experience.

Bookmarks
Get quick access to your favourite websites.

the iPhone and carry on with another device if you would like. That compatibility doesn't extend to your Mac for the iBooks though, but it does for the Kindle. Not all titles are available in digital form as of yet, but there's enough there to keep you busy for days.

– if not betters – the likes of the Nintendo DS and PlayStation's PSP.

There really is no shortage of options available, and everyone's tastes are covered. The only problem you may have is deciding what to play on when you're next on that long train journey!

Games

When it comes to games, you'll be spoilt for choice on the iPhone. There are so many available to download, both free or paid-for that you can spend hours getting immersed in an adventure story (thank goodness for the iPhone's excellent battery life), or just use it to while away a few minutes of your time.

The iPhone really has revolutionised the way that we play games. Just going for the obvious example, *Angry Birds* become a global smash when it was released on the App Store, with versions now available for iPad and Android and a console version on the way too. Whether it's puzzle games like this and *Cut The Rope*, or action games you're after, the iPhone has it covered. Racing games have also found a home on the iPhone, with the accelerometer allowing for easy control that rivals

Office work

The iPhone isn't just a device to browse the web, watch videos and play games however. Many people classify it as just a media consumption device, but it's in fact a very powerful machine capable of doing many things that a regular computer can. It comes with a Notes program which you can use to jot down a few ideas, lists, or even the beginning of a draft letter. That application syncs with your emails and you can access those documents in your Mac's Mail program, which is very convenient and enables you to work between the two systems.

But the iPhone can go a lot further than this. For one thing, apps such as Things act as an excellent task manager, allowing you to monitor your workflow and keep up to date with all your jobs. Documents 2 Go is just one of the apps available

"The iPhone really has revolutionised the way that we play games"

that will allow you to manage spreadsheets, and you can even download applications that will allow you to use your iPhone as an external hard drive

If you need compatibility with Microsoft Word, take a look at Office[2]. It' might not be the most attractive application in thew world, but it lets you create native Word (both .doc and .docx) and Excel (.xls) documents on your iPhone for a very reasonable price.

Productivity

As for other productivity programs, Calendar stores all your appointments and syncs with iCal on your Mac – as long as you've got a MobileMe subscription. The same applies for the Contacts app, even preserving all your groups so you'll feel right at

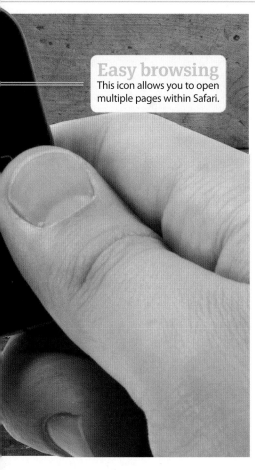

Easy browsing
This icon allows you to open multiple pages within Safari.

App Store FAQ

A vital part of the iPhone explained

What's all this talk about apps? Do I need them?

A Apps, or applications, are programs that run on a computer, like your browser or word processor. They increase your device's functionality and you should definitely browse through them to see if there's anything you might find crucial to your life on the iPhone.

Where do I get those apps?

A Straight from the App Store, which you can access from iTunes itself. You might find some websites showcasing various programs, but you can only purchase and download them from iTunes.

What if I'm just browsing? Can I find stuff easily?

A Of course: the App Store is really designed to help you buy programs. As a result, you can look through various lists like top sellers, top free apps, staff recommendations, and so on.

Is there any trial software I can use?

A Not as such, but many developers have 'lite' or 'free' versions of their applications. These offer limited functionality or a few sample levels if it's a game. If you like what you see, you can then purchase the full program and delete the lite copy.

How do I find what I want?

A With over 400,00 apps designed for the iPhone, you may feel that you may never find the exact program you need. Try using the search field to narrow down the results.

home on your new machine. You also have a built-in calculator, allowing you to crunch those numbers with ease

Another feature missing from the iPhone is any possibility of using it like an external drive, but the fantastic advantage of the iPhone and any device powered by the iOS software is the huge number of developers working on it. As a result, someone's come up with a way of achieving just that thanks to an application called USB Disk so you can easily use your iPhone like an external portable hard drive.

Chances are, whatever it is you're looking for, someone may already have designed a solution that fits your exact needs.

  WordSeek **Winnie the Pooh**

Kids

The iPhone is an amazing learning tool no matter what your age is; there's even a dedicated section called "Apps for Kids" in the App Store where you can get interactive books like *Winnie the Pooh* or *The Cat in the Hat*, programs that teach you how to read and write or even understand the world around you, help you play music, draw, … pretty much anything you can imagine. You'll also find

Can I only get them from my computer?

A No: there's a program called 'App Store' on your iPhone. From there, you can gain access to the entire store as well, and the beauty of the iPhone is that with a 3G connection you'll be able to download wherever you are.

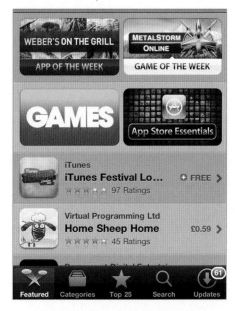

It's all a bit of a jumble; can I narrow my search down?

A The App Store is broken into 20 categories, each with its own top sellers list. You can narrow your search by focusing on a single category.

Why can't I comment on a program I'm looking at?

A In order to limit bogus reviews or overly negative or positive comments from people who've never used the program, Apple links your reviews to your account. The company can therefore check if you own the app and if you don't, you can only read, not contribute.

How can I ask questions or get help from the developer?

A At the bottom of every app description is a link to the developer's own website. More often than not, you'll find a help forum or contact email address there which you can use to write to the developer or company and get the help you need.

Why does my App Store icon have red numbers on it?

A These badges are there to show you that some of the programs you've acquired have been updated and that you can get those new versions for free directly from the App Store's Updates section on your iPhone (or computer).

>>

all of your favourite characters on the iPhone, from Igglepiggle and Thomas the Tank Engine to Buzz Lightyear and Hello Kitty.

Older children haven't been left out either: there are some fantastic apps that will help you with your algebra or other subjects that are taught at school, and the majority are easy to use and entertaining, and much more fun than sitting down in front of a work book! There are also things to keep them entertained such as wordsearch apps like WordSeek and much more

If you're interested in space, you can learn everything you need to know thanks to programs like Solar Walk or SolarSystem for iPhone, and the little ones can keep up with their older siblings with iLearn Solar System. There are so many other great learning tools available that we couldn't possibly fit them all in here, and many of them are for niche areas that almost anything you could think of is likely to be covered.

Maps

The beauty of the iPhone is that you can connect to the internet wherever you are, without having to worry about being in range of a Wi-Fi connection. There's also the added advantage of being able to use the Maps application to help you navigate to your desired location. This application will even show you areas to avoid due to traffic jams or dense circulation.

"Use the Maps application to help you navigate to your desired location"

You may get tired of hearing how "magical" the iPhone is, but it's undeniable how truly amazing it is to be able to scroll through a map and effortlessly zoom in and out of a location using your fingers alone. The program is incredibly responsive and the only limitation you'll experience will be the signal strength you're able to receive depending on your location. It illustrates just how wonderful using this device truly is. There are also other map apps available, so check out the App Store to find one that suits you. And if it's help on your travels you're after, the iPhone 4 can act as a satnav device, meaning you won't have to splash out on a separate device when all you'll really need is your ever-useful iPhone. CoPilot is one of the most popular satnav apps, and will cost you less than £20.

Accessories
Enrich your hardware with some great kit...

Cases Covers are all well and good, and may protect from the odd scratch and scrape, but if you want protection when your iPhone is in your pocket a case is what you need.

Dock
The iPhone's battery is fantastic, and it's rare that you'll run out of juice on the go, but if you want a fast, stylish way to recharge your phone, you can't go wrong with a dock.

FM Transmitter Transmitters like an iTrip make playing music in your car as simple as transmitting to a free radio frequency. It's a great way to get your music on the move.

Covers There are a huge number of covers to choose from, offering different levels of protection and style. You'll find something to suit you, so it's worth shopping around.

Bluetooth headset If you need to talk while you drive but also want to stay safe, the best solution is a Bluetooth headset. They've been around a while too, so they're not too expensive any more.

Headphones The headphones included with the iPhone aren't too bad, but if you want high-quality sound you can do a lot better. Do your research and you can get a great deal on some brilliant sound.

Speaker dock
It's easy to forget that the iPhone has an iPod built in, so to make the most of your tunes you'll need a speaker dock. Simply slot your phone in, press play, and rock out.

Car charger If you're often on the move, or find your battery regularly running low, you might want to invest in a car charger. They're simple to use and incredibly useful.

menu

Setting up

Get to grips with the basics of your iPhone

Tip 1
Sync with iTunes

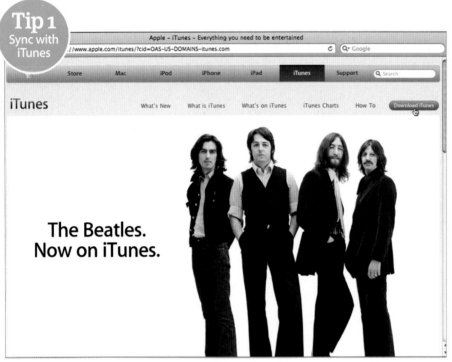

Tip 2
Import a film

Tip 3
Overview of iTunes

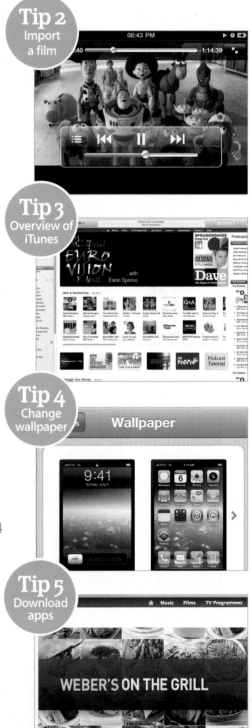

Tip 4
Change wallpaper

Tip 5
Download apps

"The iPhone is a fully fledged computer with access to the web, email, videos, hundreds of thousands of apps and more"

How to install iTunes

Unlike most other devices, Apple's iPods, iPhones and iPads don't come with any installer CDs. In order to make your device work, you need to take a trip to the internet

Despite the fact that the iPhone is a powerful device in its own right, you cannot turn it on and start using it as soon as you unpack it. Just like the iPod touch and iPad, it needs to hook up with your copy of iTunes on your Mac or PC before you can do anything else. The good news is that once you've connected it and your iPhone is set up, you can choose never to perform that action again since you can get everything you need directly from the web. But you can't bypass this crucial first step.

To set up the iPhone, you need the latest version of iTunes, namely 10.1 or above. So even if you already own a copy of iTunes, if it isn't recent, you may have to get online and update it before it'll recognise the iPhone as a valid device.

Although slightly inconvenient, finding the installer program online and installing the software isn't too difficult, as we'll show you over the course of this tutorial.

"The iPhone needs to hook up with iTunes before you can do anything else"

iTunes Installing iTunes on your Mac or PC

01 Get online

Your first step is to launch your favourite web browser and point it in the direction of **www.itunes.com**. The layout of the page changes regularly, but there will be a 'Download iTunes' button somewhere within it (currently, it's located in the top-right corner of the page).

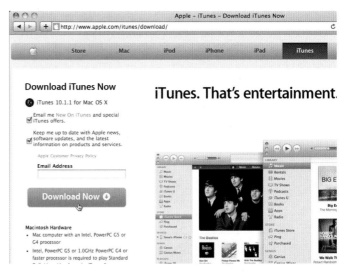

02 Download now

This will lead you to the proper download page. Your browser will recognise the type of computer you're on so you won't be offered any choices that could lead to confusion. You'll see a single 'Download Now' button. Only enter your email if you want to receive promotional messages from Apple.

The iTunes Download page

What each part of the Download page does

Automatic detection

All modern browsers transmit what type of computer you are currently using and clever websites can take advantage of that information to only offer you the choices that match those criteria

Email notifications

By default, these two tick boxes are enabled, which means that you won't be able to download iTunes without typing in your email address first. If you'd rather stay anonymous, untick them

System requirements

If you're at all uncertain if your computer will be able to run the software, this section displays the necessary system requirements that match the machine you're currently running

Privacy Policy

If you're concerned about what Apple might do with the information you give it (namely, your email address, as requested on this page), you can check out its policy by clicking here

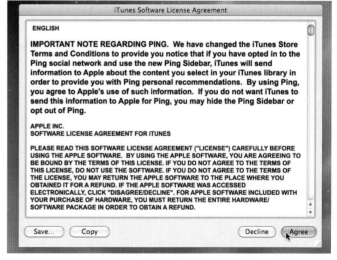

03 Installing

Once the download is complete, a new window will open up with a semi-transparent iTunes logo inside it. The 'Read Before You Install iTunes' document gives you the minimum requirements, without which the program will not function. Double-click 'Install iTunes' to proceed.

04 Licence Agreement

Once iTunes has been installed, its icon should appear in your Dock or Desktop. If it hasn't you'll be able to locate it in your Applications or Program Files folder. The first time you double-click on it, you'll have to agree to the licence agreement. Agreeing grants you access to the software.

An overview of the iTunes interface

iTunes has morphed from a program designed to look after your music library to one capable of storing any media you'd care to enjoy, all while being the gateway to Apple's online store

The first version of iTunes was released a decade ago, back on 9 January 2001. Apple had purchased Casady and Greene's SoundJam MP two years previously, realising that it had missed the boat with regards to the CD ripping and burning that was going on at the time. Back then, the iPod didn't even exist. Three years later, the iTunes Music Store was born, along with Apple's ambitions as an online entertainment retailer.

Today, you can't even start using your iPhone without connecting it to your copy of iTunes first. Alongside its original duty of managing your growing media libraries, it's become the portal through which you can access everything you need for all your iOS devices (iPod touch, iPhone and iPad), even down to upgrading their system software.

This tutorial is designed to help you understand where everything iPhone-related can be found within the iTunes interface, with a particular emphasis on locating the apps you want in the iTunes Store.

"It's the portal through which you can access everything you need"

iTunes Getting to know the software

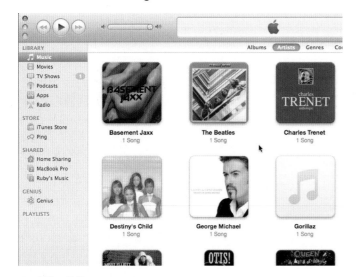

01 The Library

Your media is broken down by type, like music, films, television shows, podcasts, books and apps for your iOS devices, all of which you can acquire from the iTunes Store. The last one on the list, Radio, lets you listen to online radio stations for free.

02 The Store

To access Apple's online media store, move your cursor to the Store section in the Sidebar and click on iTunes Store. The front page is geared towards entertainment, showing you the latest and most popular songs and albums, films and TV shows (books can only be purchased from your iOS device).

Browsing the App Store

Helping you find the apps you need in seconds

Categories
Narrow down your search by browsing through a specific category. To access this menu, click on the small triangle to the right of 'App Store'

Search and find
If none of these are of any help, you can always use the good old-fashioned search field. Start typing and a list of options will appear for you to choose from

New & Noteworthy
Sometimes a recommendation is all you need, and the New & Noteworthy section shows you a selection of staff favourites that you may feel suit your exact needs

Top Charts
Looking at the bestselling apps can help you decide what to get. This one on the front page shows the top sellers irrespective of their category (categories also have their own charts)

Knowledge base
How do I choose what to add to my iPhone?

By default, iTunes is designed to take care of that for you: even if you have more media than can fit in your iPhone, it'll choose which ones to add, and which to leave behind. But if you'd like more control over the process, start by clicking on the iPhone in the Devices section. From there, you'll have options in the various tabs to select which songs, films or apps you'd like to include. There are multiple ways of doing this, which will be explained in other parts of this book.

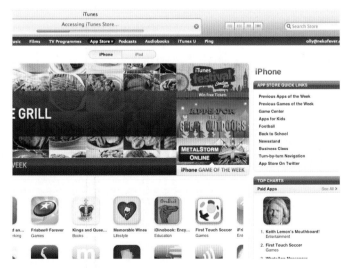

03 Finding the apps

To get to the App Store and start browsing for programs for your iPhone, check out the menu bar, top of the main part of the iTunes interface, and click on App Store. Once there, you'll find two buttons at the top, one labelled iPhone, the other iPad. Click on iPhone.

04 Connecting your iPhone

After activating your iPhone (see pages 24 and 25), it'll appear in the Sidebar under the Devices section. Click on its name and you'll gain access to your device. You can use that section to select which media to add and which apps to install, or just let iTunes add everything automatically.

Activate & register your iPhone

Until registered and activated using iTunes, an iPhone cannot be fully used.
Follow us over the next two pages as we explain how it's done

The iPhone is a fully fledged computer with full access to the web, email, videos, hundreds of thousands of apps, and more. It's the perfect device for anyone looking for an efficient way to access the web wherever you are, and it's a pretty great phone as well. However, as we've already said, the iPhone does not fully work out of the box until the device is activated and registered using iTunes. This can be done by an Apple employee within an Apple Store, but for anyone who buys the device online or in a typical retail store, a desktop computer or laptop will need to be used to get the iPhone up and running.

Thankfully, activating and registering an iPhone takes mere minutes. All that's needed is a Mac or PC with a working connection to the web and the latest version of iTunes, as we're about to explain…

"The iPhone does not work out of the box until the device is activated and registered using iTunes"

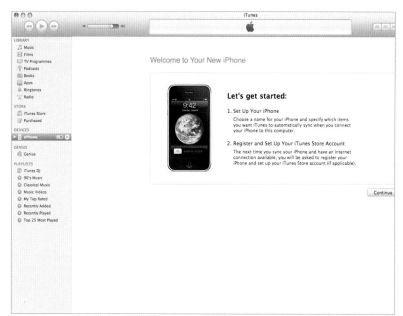

iTunes Activating your iPhone

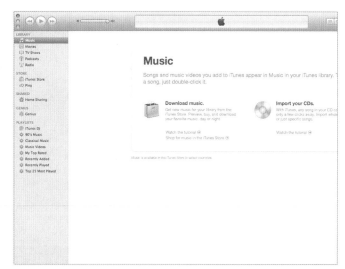

01 Turn on

Take your brand new iPhone out of its box and turn it on by pressing the button on top of the device. Next, turn on a PC or Mac and open iTunes. If you don't already have a copy installed, or you need to update to the latest version, it can be downloaded for free from **www.apple.com/itunes**.

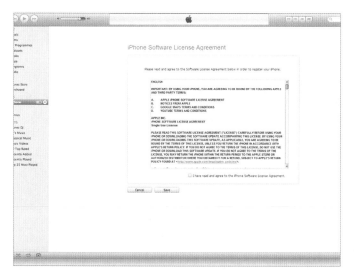

02 Plug in and set up

Once iTunes has been opened, plug your iPhone into the computer using the USB cable. iTunes will automatically detect the device and launch the activation window. You'll need to read Apple's terms and conditions, so once you're happy click on the Accept button at the bottom of the page.

Discover the basics of syncing

Find your way around the Devices section of iTunes

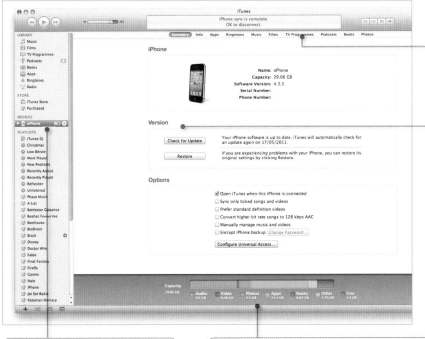

Tab buttons
The ten buttons at the top of the screen give you quick access to various syncing options, including apps, music, films, TV shows and photos

Summary
This window gives an overview of your iPhone. At the top of the screen are the device's version number and serial. Below you'll find options for syncing and backup

Library
Whenever your iPhone is plugged into a computer it will appear in the grey panel located on the left-hand side of the screen

Capacity
At the bottom of the screen is a breakdown of the files stored on your iPhone. It's a great way to see what files are using the most space, especially for those with the 16GB model

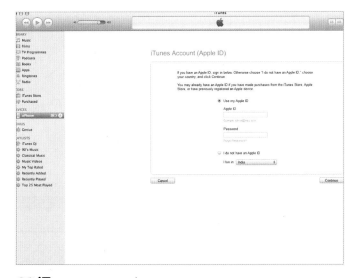

03 iTunes account
You'll be asked to log in using your iTunes account. Don't worry if you don't already have one as it's free to create a new account. Once complete, iTunes will ask if you would like to automatically sync applications, photos, music and videos.

04 Syncing
Click yes to automatically sync every picture, video and music track on the computer. If you're using a friend's machine or would rather choose which files to sync, deselect this option. Click OK and the activation process will complete. Congratulations, your iPhone is now ready to use!

Sync email, contacts and bookmarks

Never lose an email, contact or web browser bookmark by syncing all three through iTunes. Here's how easy it is…

Syncing through iTunes might seem like an inconvenience at times, but it's a really great way to ensure that you never lose any personal data, apps, files or documents. That's because every time your iPhone is plugged into the computer and synced, every file is backed up on your desktop computer. As a result, if you require a new device or buy a second iPhone you can sync it via iTunes and automatically copy every file into its correct place. It's also great for peace of mind to know that if your iPhone gets lost or stolen, those important contact details and documents remain safe and sound on your desktop machine. It really doesn't take a huge amount of time and it's one of those things that you don't really appreciate until you lose all your data, so why not avoid any unwanted hassle?

You may already be aware that music, movies, TV shows, and apps are backed up on your computer with every sync, but did you also know that contacts, emails and bookmarks are also synced? It's a great timesaver when setting up a new device, removing the need to manually type every contact from your address book, setting up email accounts and browser bookmarks. These are things that can become extremely monotonous if you're a keen gadget fan and have to perform the same tasks every time you buy a new handset. Thankfully the iPhone does all the hard work for you.

Follow us over the next two pages as we explain how to properly sync these important files and give you a breakdown of the sync screen so you know what's going on around you and what everything means.

> ## "It's a great timesaver when setting up a new device, removing the need to manually type every contact from your address book"

iTunes Sync everything you need

01 Email

iPhone supports syncing to Mail and Outlook accounts. To sync either of these, plug your iPhone into your computer, select it from the grey bar on the left in iTunes, then click on the Info tab. You'll find a Mail accounts button on this screen that enables you to sync an email account.

02 Contacts

The iPhone can sync contacts with the Mac Address Book, Windows Contacts and Outlook. Simply sync your iPhone with iTunes, select it from the left-hand side and click on the Info tab. Windows users need to check 'Sync contacts from'; Mac users can click on 'Sync Address Book contacts'.

Syncing contacts, mail and bookmarks

Everything you need to know about the iTunes Info pane

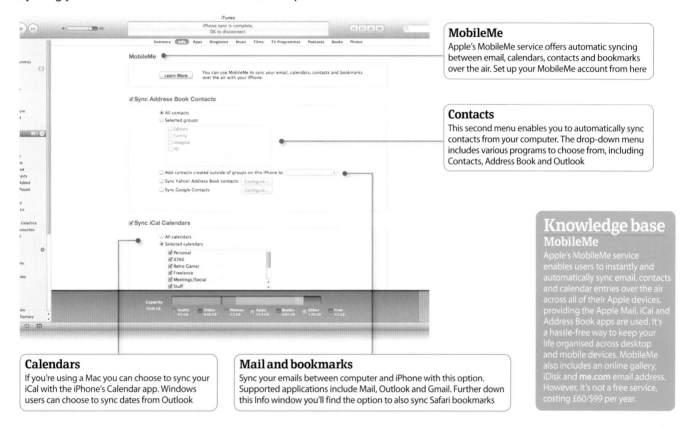

MobileMe
Apple's MobileMe service offers automatic syncing between email, calendars, contacts and bookmarks over the air. Set up your MobileMe account from here

Contacts
This second menu enables you to automatically sync contacts from your computer. The drop-down menu includes various programs to choose from, including Contacts, Address Book and Outlook

Calendars
If you're using a Mac you can choose to sync your iCal with the iPhone's Calendar app. Windows users can choose to sync dates from Outlook

Mail and bookmarks
Sync your emails between computer and iPhone with this option. Supported applications include Mail, Outlook and Gmail. Further down this Info window you'll find the option to also sync Safari bookmarks

03 Bookmarks
It's possible to sync Safari bookmarks to the iPhone. Simply sync the iPhone with iTunes, select it from the grey bar on the left again and choose the Info tab. From there, scroll down the page and check Sync Safari Bookmarks. Click Apply and every bookmark will be synced to your iPhone.

04 Sync Google contacts
Have a Google account? You can sync its contacts by selecting your iPhone from the left-hand side grey bar in iTunes then clicking on the Info tab at the top of the screen. From there, select 'Sync Address Book contacts', then click 'Sync Google Contacts' at the bottom of the list.

Sync your music collection

Here's how easy it is to sync your music collection from a computer to the iPhone

Along with the iPod touch, the iPhone is easily Apple's best music player to date. Its display makes it easy to browse the music library, album artwork looks gorgeous, and turning it sideways will enable Cover Flow, letting you flip through your music like it's on an old jukebox in your pocket. We can say with confidence that the iPhone is the most fun way to listen to music.

Getting music onto your iPhone is a simple process, done entirely through iTunes. It's possible to sync tracks, albums or your entire music library. iTunes remembers your settings, so whenever your iPhone is plugged into the computer it automatically syncs any new music tracks to the device. By spending just a few minutes setting up your music sync options, you'll never have to manually transfer tracks and albums again.

iTunes Get your music on your iPhone

01 Import tunes

First, ensure you have music tracks in your iTunes Library. Simply drag MP3 files from your computer to the iTunes interface to add them.

02 Get to your music

Plug your iPhone into your Mac or PC. Once iTunes has synced, click on your iPhone from the Library window, then click the Music tab.

03 Choose what to sync

From here you can choose what to sync. Once you're happy with the selection, click the Apply button at the bottom of the screen.

04 Get playing

Once the syncing process has been completed, turn on your iPhone and open the iPod app located in the dock at the bottom of the screen.

Sync movies onto your iPhone

We explain how easy it is to copy movies from your desktop computer to an iPhone

Movies look pretty impressive on the iPhone screen, even though it's not as big as the iPad 2. When you're on the move, the display shows off movies with vivid clarity. It gets even better if the movie has been purchased or rented through the iTunes Store, as the iPhone will let you skip directly to a particular chapter with just one tap. For those with an Apple TV it's also possible to wirelessly stream any movie to it from your iPhone,

enabling you to watch films on a high-definition TV and control the playback using the iPhone's touch screen, but more on that later.

In this tutorial we will explain how easy it is to sync movies from your desktop computer to the iPhone using the wonder that is iTunes. In next to no time you'll be up and running with a selection of great movies on your iPhone, ready to take with you on that next long journey.

iTunes Sync your movies to your iPhone

01 Get ready
Ensure you have movies to sync in iTunes. Films can be purchased from the iTunes Store, or copied to your iTunes Library in MOV or MP4 format.

02 Select films
Connect your iPhone and click on it in iTunes, then select the Films tab at the top of the screen. If unselected, check the top Sync Films button.

03 Sync!
Select the films that you wish to sync, but keep aware of the file sizes. Once you're happy, click the Apply button at the bottom of the screen.

04 Get watching
Once the films have copied you can watch them from the iPod app. If purchased from the Store, they will include chapters for easy navigation.

Copy TV shows to your iPhone

The iPhone's perfect for watching programmes on the go. Here's how to sync TV shows from a Mac/PC

With its high-res display and lengthy battery life, the iPhone is an excellent ultra-portable television. It's a great way to keep entertained on long journeys, and because the iPhone is so portable you can continue watching wherever you are in your home or elsewhere.

Getting TV shows onto your iPhone is a simple process. By opening the iTunes app you can purchase the latest episodes of your favourite show

and download them directly to the device. Alternatively it's possible to sync all the shows that are already on your desktop computer to the iPhone by using the desktop version of iTunes. Follow us through this tutorial as we explain how easy it is to sync your TV shows in just four steps. You'll have all of your favourite TV programmes ready to watch on your iPhone in no time, letting you catch up on your favourites at any time.

iTunes Watch downloaded television shows on your iPhone

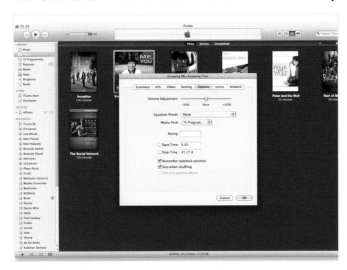

01 The right place
Click on Movies and, if any TV shows are there, right-click on them, choose Get Info then Options, and select TV Shows from the Media Kind menu.

02 Plug and sync
Plug your iPhone into the computer. Once it has synced, select it from the bar on the left. Next, click on TV Programmes at the top of the screen.

03 Select shows
If Sync TV Programmes isn't already checked, tick it to enable syncing. Once you're happy with the selection of TV shows, click the Apply button.

04 Get watching
You can view TV shows from the iPod app on your iPhone. Simply open the app and you'll see a Videos button at the bottom of the screen.

Sync podcasts onto your iPhone

Discover how to sync podcasts from your desktop computer to an iPhone

Think of podcasts as individual radio shows without the music – some are a few minutes long, others hours in length, and they can be listened to from within the iPod app on your iPhone. Once you've found a great podcast it's possible to subscribe to it from the iTunes app, enabling your device to automatically download the latest episodes as soon as they're available, ready for you to enjoy. With podcasts you can pick and choose the subjects that interest you, enabling you to skip the annoying adverts and subject matters that you normally sit through when listening to the radio.

In this tutorial we'll explain how to subscribe to podcasts and sync them to your iPhone. It's a simple process done entirely through iTunes. Once you've subscribed to a handful of podcasts you'll find yourself with hours of free entertainment, and wondering how you ever lived without them.

iTunes Listen to podcasts on your iPhone

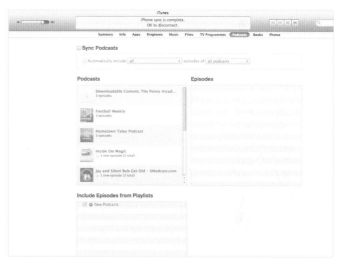

01 Download new podcasts
Open iTunes on your Mac or PC, click on the iTunes Store button then choose Podcasts from the menu at the top of the screen.

02 Plug and sync
Once you've got the podcasts, plug your iPhone into your Mac/PC. Click your iPhone from the grey side panel, then the Podcasts button at the top.

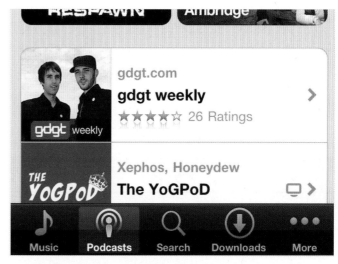

03 Syncing options
From the Podcasts window you can choose to sync individual podcasts, entire subscriptions or only the podcasts with new episodes available.

04 Podcasts on your iPhone
You can play synced podcasts from the iPod app. To get them without a Mac/PC, open the iTunes app and you'll find a Podcasts button.

Learn how to sync books

Find out how to sync books with your iPhone, and where to download the latest titles

The iPhone is a fantastic device for reading books and magazines for a number of reasons. Its incredibly sharp display makes reading text a joy, and the vivid colour screen makes images look even better than their printed counterparts. Its support for multimedia means videos and web links can be also be embedded in books, and it's also possible to change the font and text size to make the experience more personal and easier for your reading

enjoyment. There's the ability to look up words with a dictionary and easily control the brightness for when reading in a low-lit environment. The list goes on and on.

eBooks can either be synced from a computer, purchased directly from Apple's iBooks app or from the many other book apps on the App Store. In this tutorial we'll take a look at the former method, and explain how easy it is.

iTunes Sync eBooks to your iPhone

01 Drag and drop

Simply drag an ePUB or PDF file from your computer's desktop to the main window of iTunes. A Books tab will automatically be created in the Library.

02 Books window

Turn on your iPhone and plug it into the computer. After syncing, click on your iPhone from the side bar, then the Books option at the top.

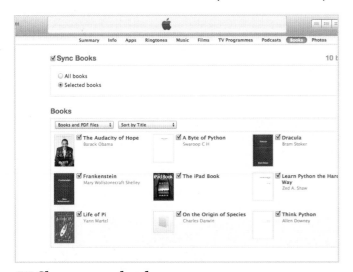

03 Choose your books

You can sync every book by checking the All Books button, or alternatively select your books of choice. Click the Apply button once you're ready.

04 iBooks

You can also download books from the iBooks app, found on the home screen of your device. For more information go to page 104.

Sync photos on your iPhone

Discover how easy it is to sync photographs from your Mac/PC to an iPhone

The iPhone is an excellent device for displaying photos. Thanks to its Multi-Touch support it's easy to swipe through images and zoom into areas where you want to explore the details. It's by far the best way to show off your latest holiday snaps as the device can be passed from person to person, and because the Photos app is so intuitive it can be used by anyone – even children.

There are a handful of ways to get your favourite photos onto your iPhone. They can be synced from a Mac/PC, emailed or saved from the web. In this tutorial we'll explain how easy it is to transfer images from your computer using iTunes. It only takes a few clicks, and because iTunes re-syncs images every time you plug the iPhone into your Mac/PC you'll never have to manually transfer photos again.

iTunes Get your photos on your iPhone

01 Plug in
Open iTunes on your Mac/PC, then plug the iPhone into the computer and they'll sync. Once done, click on your iPhone from the bar on the left.

02 iPhone summary
You'll see a summary of your iPhone. At the top of the screen are various buttons for syncing media – click on the Photos button at the far end.

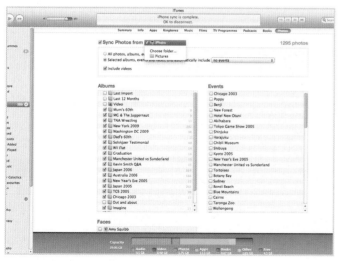

03 Choose your photos
Here you'll see an option to sync photos from your Mac or PC. Click on the check box and choose a source. When correct, click Apply.

04 Get syncing
If sub-folders or albums are present you can choose which to sync from the window below. Once you're happy, click the Apply button.

Introduction to Settings on iOS 4

Understanding how to personalise your device can make all the difference. We show you how to make important choices

iOS 4 is actually a highly configurable system, and we don't just mean that you can change your wallpaper, though of course you can! The default settings that it has when you first fire it up are pretty good for most people, but there will surely be something that you would like it to do differently, whether it's waiting a little longer before locking the screen, remembering your passwords in Safari or adding a signature to your outgoing Mail messages. More or less all of the iOS apps like Mail, Messages, iPod, photos and the phone section of an iPhone can be tweaked and tuned to behave as you like, whether it's using shake to shuffle on the iPod player or automatically checking for mail.

You can't alter everything of course, and though some people claim that this is a bad thing, quite the opposite is true. On mobile phones and tablets that do let you endlessly muck about with every part of the system, the result is almost always a terrible, unusable mess. iOS gives you just enough room to personalise your device while making sure that you don't end up actually making things worse.

"All of the iOS apps can be tweaked and tuned to behave as you like"

iOS settings The basics

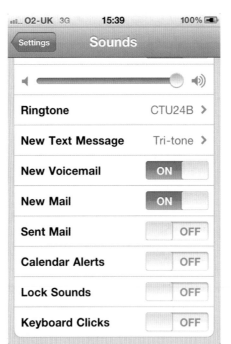

01 Go to Settings

Hit the Settings icon on your Home screen to go to the Settings section. The options are grouped into categories, including connectivity and appearance.

02 Customise sounds

Go into the Sounds section. Here you can set your ringtone tune and specify whether sounds should play when you get a new mail or voicemail.

03 Set wallpaper

In the Wallpaper section you can choose an image or pick one from your camera roll, then set one image for the Home and Lock screens, or one for each.

Manage your iPhone's settings

Most of your phone's functions can be customised

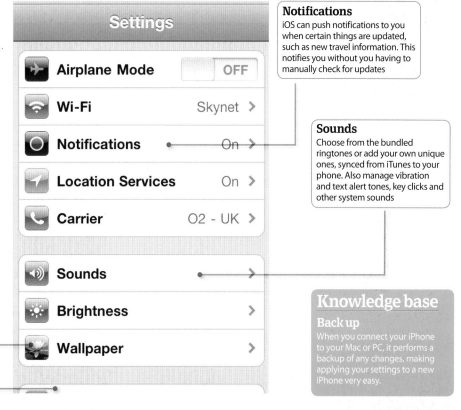

Settings

Airplane Mode — OFF

Wi-Fi — Skynet >

Notifications — On >

Location Services — On >

Carrier — O2 - UK >

Sounds >

Brightness >

Wallpaper >

Notifications
iOS can push notifications to you when certain things are updated, such as new travel information. This notifies you without you having to manually check for updates

Sounds
Choose from the bundled ringtones or add your own unique ones, synced from iTunes to your phone. Also manage vibration and text alert tones, key clicks and other system sounds

Wallpaper
Alter the wallpaper and choose from Apple's images or any picture from your image library or camera roll. Choose separate wallpapers for the Home and Lock screens if you like

General settings
All the stuff that doesn't fit elsewhere, including serial numbers, data usage, Bluetooth, auto lock, passcodes and more. A very important section to know about

Knowledge base

Back up
When you connect your iPhone to your Mac or PC, it performs a backup of any changes, making applying your settings to a new iPhone very easy.

04 Phone section

Here you can turn FaceTime on or off, set up call forwarding and waiting, change your voicemail password and activate a PIN code for your SIM card.

05 Set up Safari

By default, Safari blocks pop-up windows, which is handy. In this section you can also get it to autofill forms and passwords, which are stored securely in your iPhone's keychain.

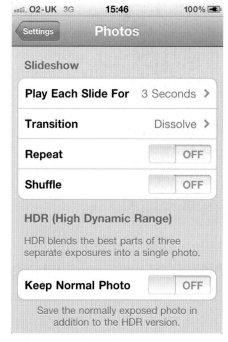

06 Photos section

Here you can choose how slideshows should behave – how long each slide plays for, what transition is used and if the playback shuffles or loops.

How to set up Wi-Fi

There are a host of services on the iPhone, but you'll need to get online. We show you how to do just that

For all the iPhone's uses and versatility, it doesn't really come into its own until you have Wi-Fi access. Sure you can play games, write documents, send emails and even download the latest books, but you can't do the really big stuff if you don't have Wi-Fi access to the internet.

Internet access turns your iPhone from an impressive piece of expensive kit into something that opens up worlds. This in part is due to the magnificence that is the App Store, a virtual store that gives you access to literally thousands of different applications, ranging from popular games like *Angry Birds* and *Real Racing* to GPS devices, interactive encyclopaedias, word processing apps and much, much more.

Your iPhone is a portal to a host of fantastic services, but first you need to give it access to the internet – then your options become plentiful. Follow our simple instructions in this easy-to-follow tutorial and unleash the potential of Apple's powerful device. You won't regret it.

Settings Switch on Wi-Fi on your iPhone

01 Getting started
Go to the very first page of your iPhone and look for the icon featuring one large cog and two small ones. Once found tap it once to enter your settings.

02 Locate Wi-Fi
After entering Settings, the second option down is Wi-Fi. Tap on it and then turn Wi-Fi on by sliding the button.

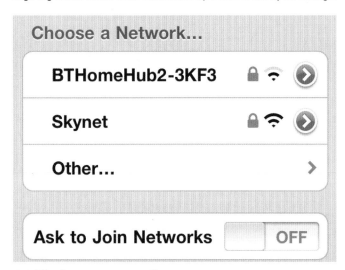

03 Find your connection
Your iPhone will now start looking for available connection points. Ignore Ask to Join Networks at the bottom and simply tap on your connection.

04 The final hurdle
You are now ready to enter your Wi-Fi password. Fill in your details on the keyboard. Once filled in select Join on the virtual keyboard and you're done.

How to set up 3G

Access the internet while away from your home

3G is a network service that allows you to access the internet while away from a Wi-Fi signal. It's an amazingly useful service, due to the fact that as communication networks expand, online access is becoming more expensive. While public Wi-Fi spots are becoming more numerous – everywhere from pubs to McDonalds has them, and many are free – there can still be charges.

3G access comes with all iPhones and is enabled by default, which means you can access the internet wherever you happen to be, whether there's a Wi-Fi signal or not. However, if you're going abroad or looking to save on battery life, it's a good idea to know how to tweak your settings, as sometimes you may want to avoid roaming charges or use up your data allowance unnecessarily. Follow these simple steps to set up your 3G.

Settings Change your iPhone's 3G settings

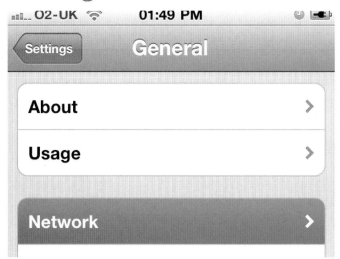

01 Find your settings
In the Settings app, find the General category and tap it. In here, tap Network to find your 3G settings.

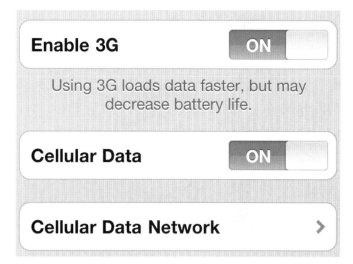

02 Network settings
You can toggle 3G on or off at the top of the screen. Your battery will last longer with it off, but your data connection will be limited to slower speeds.

03 Data roaming
Using 3G while abroad can rack up massive charges, so the Data Roaming option is of interest to budget-conscious travellers.

04 Don't forget
Unless you have an international roaming package, keep it turned off. You'll need Wi-Fi to get online, but you'll avoid nasty surprises on your bill.

Learn how to access email on your iPhone

Having your email with you wherever you go makes it invaluable. This handy tutorial will let you set up your own personal account

In today's digital age, using email is one of the most essential ways of being able to stay in touch with friends and family, as well as being a pretty vital tool in the business world. The ability to take your messages with you wherever you go on your iPhone makes it even more essential, and means you're not limited to responding whenever you happen to be able to log in to your main email account. Important business can be taken care of as soon as it arrives, and you never need to worry about what could be waiting for you when you finally get back to your desktop.

This step-by-step tutorial will not only show you how to set up a new or existing email account for use on the iPhone and beyond, but will also take you through the fundamentals of reading and sending email. Once set up you'll be able to use existing accounts at will, whether your business or personal accounts, or freebies from the likes of Google or Yahoo!.

You'll be able to reply to and forward mail that you receive and, most importantly, ensure that you stay in touch with friends and loved ones, no matter where they – or you – might be. Basically, you will never look at stodgy old email in the same way again, so read on to learn how to master email on the move and free yourself from your desk at work or home.

"The ability to take your messages with you wherever you go on your iPhone makes email even more essential"

Settings   Set up an email account on your iPhone

01 Setting things up

In order to set up an email account you will need to first enter the Settings of your iPhone. Look at the icons on your iPhone's Home screen until you find one with a large cog and two smaller cogs. Tap on it to continue to the Settings menu.

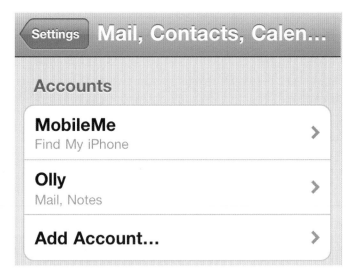

02 Finding your mail

Upon entering Settings scroll down until you find the section headed by the General settings. Look for and select 'Mail, Contacts, Calendars' in order to continue. On the next screen, locate and tap on Add Account…

Viewing mail

How to navigate your messages in Mail

Send email
Tap the button in the bottom right-hand corner of the screen to send mail. Fill out the address, add a subject and write your mail. Hit Send when you're finished

Forwarding mail
If you need to reply to an email hit the arrow icon near the bottom of the screen. You can then reply to the sender or forward the message on

Move items
Want to organise your mail? Simply tap the folder icon located at the bottom of the screen. You can then send your mail to a variety of different folders

Knowledge base
Adding more accounts
If you have the need for additional accounts (perhaps a work account or the account of your significant other) it's relatively easy to add them. All you need to do is re-follow the previous steps for setting up an account. Once you've done that when you enter your mail you will see an 'Accounts' tab in the top left-hand side of the screen. Simply tap on this tab to be taken to all the other accounts set up on your iPhone. Select the one you want and you can instantly access your other mail. Very handy.

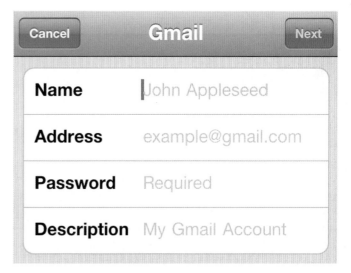

03 Make your choice
You'll now be presented with six different account options. They are Microsoft Exchange, MobileMe, Google Mail, Yahoo! Mail, AOL and Other (which will allow you access accounts like Hotmail). Whether you want to create a new account or add an existing one the process is as follows…

04 You've got mail!
After choosing your account you'll be presented with the following screen. All you need to do here is fill in the relevant information for each section. Once this is done simply tap on Next in the top right-hand corner. Congratulations, you have mail.

Change Wallpaper on your iPhone

We show you how to quickly customise the background of your Home and lock screens

With the iPhone, Apple has allowed users the ability to change the background of the Home screen as well as the lock screen. This may seem like a trivial addition to the software set but for Apple it's pretty big. It is a company that deals in absolutes and employs a closed system to prevent people making the environment look bad. So we're glad that we get to add a little individuality, and we're also pretty pleased when we discovered you can also have different images for the lock and Home screens.

Making changes to the system is very simple. Proficiency at this simple task should give you the courage to explore the settings further to get even more use from your iPhone and make improvements to the way it works for you.

Whether it's an image from the iPhone's supplied Wallpaper set or a photo from your album or camera roll – even one that you've saved from the web – following this step-by-step tutorial will instantly customise your iPhone and have it looking the way you want it to.

"Add a little individuality with customised wallpaper from your camera roll"

Settings Change wallpaper

01 Cog tapper

Load the settings by tapping the Settings button in the iPhone Home screen. You will be taken to this screen. Tap on Wallpaper at the bottom of the second section.

02 Wallpaper

These are the backgrounds that you can change: lock screen on the left and the Home screen on the right. When you're ready to change them, tap the image to continue.

03 Options

You now have several options from which to pick a picture. Choose the album that you wish to pick from. Tap on that album to then bring up the contents.

Customising your Home screen

Making the most of your iPhone's screen

Wallpaper Preview

Finger fun
While positioning your picture you'll be able to see just how responsive the iPhone's touch screen is. It's a testament to hardware and software unity

Kill it
Apple also makes it easy for you to change your mind and go back to the last action. In this case just hit the Cancel button

Make your choice
Once you're happy with the image you want as your background, tap on the Set button and the chosen picture will appear

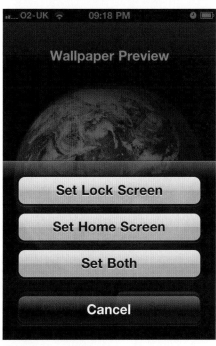

04 Preview
Once in the album of your choice, make your final selection and then simply tap on that picture. A zooming animation will automatically take you to a preview screen.

05 Scale and set
Use a pinch, reverse pinch and swipe to position the image and then tap Set. You'll be able to pick Set Lock Screen, Set Home Screen or Set Both in the pop-up prompt.

06 Check it
Once you've tapped an option you'll be taken back to the home screen where you can see your changes. Use the sleep button if you wish to view the lock screen.

Getting started

Covering everything you need to
get up and running on your iPhone

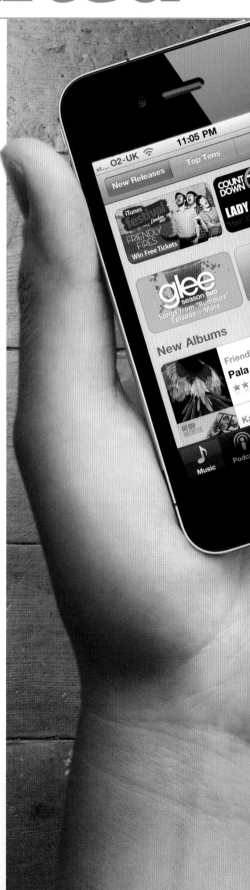

Tip 1
Read an eBook

Tip 2
Browse the web

Tip 3
Download music

At Great Prices

Foo Fighters
Foo Fighters: Greatest Hits
★★★★☆ 339 Ratings

Noah & The Whale
Last Night On Earth
★★★★☆ 311 Ratings

Lady GaGa
The Fame Monster
★★★★☆ 2763 Ratings

P!nk
Greatest Hits...So Far!!!

"You have the freedom to download and store your favourite songs on your iPhone"

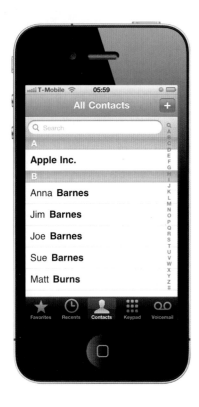

Call a person from your contacts

Simple steps on how to locate contact details and then make a call from your iPhone

Calling a contact from your iPhone is simple, and takes advantage of one of the device's most basic but most essential and commonly used tasks. Once you have added all of your contact details onto your iPhone it will automatically store them in alphabetical order, making it easy to search and call a specific name and number from your contacts list without having to trawl through endless entries.

You can also use your iPhone's Voice Control feature to locate and call contacts hands-free, and there's a more in-depth tutorial explaining how to do this over on page 47.

Here are some simple, easy to follow steps on how to locate your contacts list and then make a call directly from their information, and when it's this easy you may find it hard to stop ringing people at all hours of the day!

> "Once you have added all of your contact details onto your iPhone it will store them in alphabetical order"

Contacts   Search for and call a contact

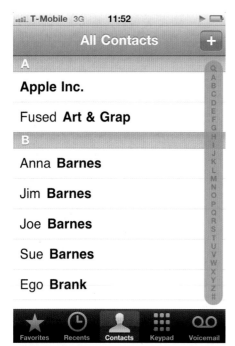

01 Phone menu

Select the Phone icon from the Home screen. This will take you into the phone call out menu. Select the Contacts icon along the bottom bar to bring up all of your contacts in alphabetical order.

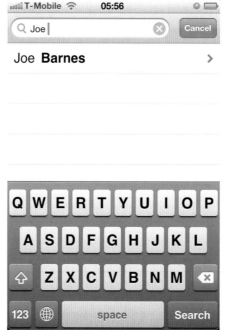

02 Search for a contact

Using the alphabet down the right-hand side of the screen select the first letter of the last name you wish to select and call. Alternatively you can use the search bar at the top of the page.

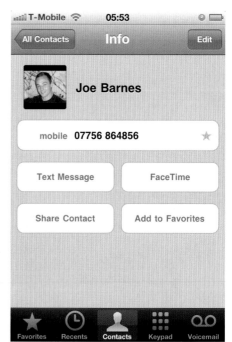

03 Make a call

Once you have located your contact's name tap on it, this will take you onto their information page. Select their phone number (either mobile or home) to make the call.

Dial a call using the keypad

Use your iPhone's keypad to dial a phone number that you don't have stored in your Contacts

Using your iPhone's keypad to dial phone numbers and make quick direct calls to people you don't have listed in your contacts is one of the iPhone's main features. This is the same for any mobile phone and works in an almost universal way.

The feature is easy to use; once you have selected the Phone icon from the Home screen you can enter in a number and even add it into your contacts if you wish. The iPhone's intuitive Voice Control feature can also be used to dial a call hands-free when on the go.

Follow along with these three simple steps to access your iPhone's keypad and dial out to make a call. It may be a simple function but it's one that you'll use a lot.

"Once you've selected the Phone icon you can enter in a number and even add it into your contacts if you wish"

Keypad Dial a call using the keypad

01 Loading the keypad
Begin by selecting the Phone icon from the Home screen. Your iPhone should now open the keypad, however you can also select the keypad icon if you need to from the bottom bar menu.

02 Dialling numbers
Once the keypad menu is open you can begin typing in the number. You can also add the number to your contacts by clicking the Add Contact icon to the left of the Call button.

03 Calling out
Once you have typed in the required phone number press the green Call button to begin dialling out. This will take you to the dial out screen, you can end the call by tapping End.

Set up Call Waiting

Receive another call while you are on the phone and avoid sending them to voicemail by using Call Waiting

Call Waiting is fantastic for organising and managing your incoming calls. Once set up your iPhone will alert you to incoming calls while you are already on the phone, allowing you to opt to put your current call on hold and answer the incoming call if you either deem that call more important or want to let the person know that you're on another line and that you'll ring them back when you're finished.

If the Call Waiting setting is switched off, your phone will automatically send the incoming call to voicemail so that you can play the message and call back another time. But sometimes you may not want to use this option if you're waiting for a particularly important call. You can also use Call Waiting to put your current caller on hold and make a second call from your iPhone simply by selecting the Add Call icon, allowing you to select a contact number or dial one via the keypad.

To set up Call Waiting and receive a second incoming call or add another, follow the simple steps below.

"Your iPhone will alert you to incoming calls while you are already on the phone, allowing you to put your call on hold"

Call Waiting
Using Call Waiting to receive new calls

01 Set up Call Waiting
To set up Call Waiting, go to Settings>Phone, click on Call Waiting and switch to On. You can now receive incoming calls and put current calls on hold without your iPhone switching to voicemail.

02 Receive a new call
While on a call your iPhone will beep if you receive another call. A menu gives you the option to either ignore (send to voicemail), Hold Call + Answer or End Call + Answer.

03 Switching between calls
You can switch between calls using Swap or by tapping on the contact's name at the top of the screen, putting the other caller on hold. You can end each call by selecting the End button.

Using Voice Control

Learn how to use voice commands to make calls and play songs from your iPhone

T he iPhone 4 comes with voice control capabilities that allow you to access music on your iPod or make calls using some simple voice command controls.

Fantastic for hands-free use, particularly when driving, voice commands can be recognised from the iPhone and headset microphone simply by speaking clearly and using the phone the same way in which you would if you were making a call. Your iPhone's Voice Control feature can also be set up your suit your language preference and is sensitive to accents, making it accessible to all users.

Follow along with our three simple steps below to set up and start using your iPhone's excellent Voice Control feature.

Recognised voice commands

Use the follow voice commands to correctly operate Voice Control

Get help with Voice Control: Say "Help".
Exit Voice Control: Use "Cancel".

To a make a phone call using Voice Control, follow along with these commands:
To make a call from your contacts: Say "Dial" or "Call" after the beep then add the contact's name (ie "Call John Smith"). **Note:** If the contact has two numbers one being a mobile and the other a home number include this in the voice command (ie "Call John Smith Mobile" or "Call John Smith at Home").

Dial a number: "Dial" or "Call" after the beep and then add in the number (ie "Call 078954763").

Correct mistakes: Use the words "No", "Not that", "Nope" or "Not that one" to correct any mistakes that you make.

To use Voice Control for music playback and iPod functions, use the following commands:
Play an album, artist or playlist: "Play" or "Play music". You can also use "Pause" or "Pause music" to put the music on hold and use "Next song" or "Previous song" to move along.

Shuffle the play list or album: Use "Shuffle".
Get information on the song playing: Use "What song is this", "What's playing" or "Who sings this song".

Play similar songs: Say "Genius" or "Play more songs like this" or "Play more like this".

Voice Control Set up and start using Voice Control

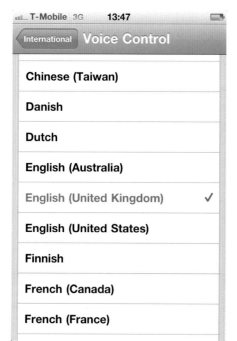

01 Setting up voice control
Ensure Voice Control is set up correctly by selecting the Settings icon. Scroll through the menu to 'General' and select 'International'. Tap on Voice Control and select a suitable language.

02 Activate Voice Control
Ensure you're on the home screen. Hold down the Home button, this will bring up the Voice Control display. If you're using earphones you can hold the centre button to activate Voice Control.

03 Using Voice Control
Once you have held down the Home button and the voice control screen appears wait until you hear a double-beep to begin talking. You can now follow along with the listed commands.

Muting your calls

Learn how to respect quiet areas and public places by muting, and retrieving your calls at the touch of your iPhone's Mute icon

We've all been caught out by unexpected phone calls we simply can't afford not to answer when we've been in a quiet place, social event or public area. When hanging up or ignoring the call isn't an option, the next best option available to you is muting the person on the other end while you find a private place to continue your potentially disruptive conversation. The process is simple really.

Whenever a call comes through that you need to mute, simply tap the mute icon in the top left of the keypad to turn the caller volume off completely. To bring back caller audio, simply tap the icon again to turn it back up.

Alternatively, you can also mute your iPhone's volume completely by flipping the switch on the top left of the device down for mute and up to restore the volume. However, if you simply want to turn the volume down a touch, you can use the volume bar, which is on the left of the device. It's a simple process that can be initiated at short notice while on a call.

"You can also mute your iPhone's volume completely by flipping the switch on the top left of the device"

Mute Key Initiate the mute command

01 Start your call
The keypad appears when a call has begun, specifically after the person's answered. From here you can access commands, including the Mute key. It's located on the top left.

02 Activate Mute key
When tapping the Mute key, you turn down the volume of the person on the other end of the line, however you can still speak to the caller, perhaps to tell them to hold the line for a second.

03 Deactivate Mute key
Pressing the Mute key again will return the caller volume back to its previous level. Bear in mind that the mute process does not disconnect calls, it simply cancels out the audio temporarily.

Expanding your keypad

Get more from your on-screen keypad during a call, by using these simple steps, and letting you activate touch tone-enabled automated menu systems

When calling a bank or other phone-based customer service, you will need to use your iPhone's touch tone options to access menu options, or input account information before proceeding. The iPhone lets you perform this function from the top caller menu. Simply make a call and connect to the help line or service and the caller menu will appear.

From there, you need to tap the keypad icon to bring up the expanded key set, which houses the typical phone numbers from one to nine, as well as the star and hash key. Like a landline handset, each time you tap a number or symbol, your iPhone will emit a touch tone sound to indicate when an icon has been pressed.

When you are done inputting digits, you can simply tap the red end icon to finish the call, or tap the hide keypad function to return back to the call menu. Using this keypad will in no way cut off your call.

"Like a landline handset, your iPhone will emit a touch tone sound to indicate when an icon has been pressed"

Keypad Using your expanded keypad

01 Place a call
To access the expanded keypad, you need to place a call. You can pre-empt the automated options by pressing the keypad icon on the call menu as soon as the call connects.

02 Access the keypad
After tapping the keypad icon, you can input numbers or symbols without disrupting your call. As a handy tip, you can also take down numbers dictated to you over the phone in this field.

03 Close the keypad
Once you're done, hit the red 'End' icon, or tap Hide Keypad to return to the call menu. You don't need to worry about deleting all the numbers as they will go when you leave the menu.

Using your speaker

If you want other people to listen to what a caller is saying, you can place them on speaker, amplifying the volume for all to hear

If the person on the other end of the line has good news, an announcement or something they want to share with a group of people at one time, you can place them on speaker, which amplifies the volume of the call by using the iPhone's in-built speaker. Not only will this boost the volume of the caller significantly, the level of the call can also be tweaked precisely by using the iPhone's volume bar on the left-hand side of the device.

If you want to take a call off this mode, all you need to do is tap speaker again and the audio returns to normal levels. This won't cut off the call, but it will require you to hold the iPhone up to your ear again to hear what the caller is saying. Hopping in and out of speaker mode won't cause any loss in call quality or accidentally cancel the call, so feel free to boost or lower the volume as often as you like without fear of hanging up on the other person by mistake.

> "Not only will this boost the volume of the caller significantly, the level of the call can also be tweaked precisely by using the iPhone's volume bar"

Speaker function Placing calls on speaker

01 Connect a call
Accessing the speaker function requires you to connect a call first. For example, you cannot use the function to amplify music or other audio. Place your call and wait for it to connect.

02 Turn on speaker
When the call is connected, hit the speaker icon in the top left of the screen to amplify the person on the other end. Speaker overrides whatever volume you had set before you pressed the icon.

03 Turn off speaker
Tapping the speaker icon again will return the call to its normal volume. This is whatever volume you had the call at previously. It won't, under any circumstances, disconnect the call.

Making a new call

Group conversations or juggling multiple calls at once may sound like a tricky prospect, but it's actually incredibly simple, thanks to the iPhone's new call function

If you need to speak to more than a single person at once, or to start a group discussion to work out travel plans or conduct other, more complicated phone calls, it is possible to start a new call while already connected to another person on the line. You can also merge more than one caller into a call conference. To get started, simply place your first call and wait for the person to answer.

Once connected, simple tap the new call button to head to your contact book. From here you can search your contacts for another person to bring into the call. Tap the name of the contact and the phone will ring again, still with the first person on the line. Once the second person is connected, you can jump between each line in private or open up the call to a group conversation by tapping the merge key. It's simple and doesn't disrupt call quality,

"Once the second person is connected, you can jump between each line in private or open up the call to a group conversation by tapping the merge key"

New call Making a secondary call

01 Place the first call
To get started, call up your first contact as normal and wait for them to connect. When the caller menu pops up, simply tap the new call icon and wait for your address book to appear on screen.

02 Place new call
From your contact book, find the next person you want to invite into the conversation and tap their name to phone them. The original caller will remain on the line while you are doing this.

03 Merge the call
You can either switch between both callers by tapping the swap icon, or combine contacts by tapping merge calls. By doing the latter, all three of you can talk to each other at once as a group.

Holding your calls

Putting people on hold is ideal if you have to search for information or do things while on the line

While muting callers will render the audio coming from their end silent, they will still be able to hear you on the other end. This is not an ideal situation, especially if you have something private to discuss with someone off the line. Placing callers on hold is a neat counter to this, and is useful when you need to cancel out the audio between both sides of the call altogether. You do not need to worry about cutting the caller off completely, as it simply affects the audio of the call, not the actual phone connection itself.

To begin the process, you must make sure the person on the other end has connected. You can tell when the call is active when the on-screen keypad comes up on your screen. The hold button is designated by a pause symbol in the middle on the bottom row of the keypad. Simply tap the icon to place the caller on hold. They will hear silence on their end until you hit the icon again and bring them back into the call. Again, this will not close the call or kick the other person off the line under any circumstances, all it does is simply halt the audio temporarily.

"This will not close the call or kick the other person off the line under any circumstances"

Hold key Placing calls on hold

01 Place your call

Holding is two-way which means you can either be the person placing the call, or the recipient. Both parties can place the other on hold if they need to, and bring each other back in.

02 Hold the call

To place a person on hold, hit the Hold key, which is designated on screen by a pause symbol. The audio will then cut out on both ends temporarily until the key is tapped again.

03 Resume the call

When you tap Hold a second time, the icon will go back to normal and the call volume will be restored, placing both you and the caller back on the line to continue talking.

Your contact book

Accessing your address book to retrieve important phone numbers or email information while in the middle of a call is both simple, and incredibly useful too

I t's easy to get into a muddle when you are preoccupied on a phone call, especially when the person on the other end asks you for further information that you don't necessarily have to hand. If you need to give someone an important email address or phone number that is stored in your iPhone's contact book, there's no need to fret as you can directly access it by simply making a call, then tapping the contacts icon in the bottom right of the on-screen keypad that follows.

You will then be taken directly to your iPhone's contact book while the call is still active. Now you can explore your contacts at your leisure without fear of disconnecting the call, and access the information you desire. You can also keep an eye on your call time by looking at the green call bar at the top of the screen. Simply find a contact, copy the information or make a note of it, then hit the green bar to return to the previous screen. You can do this as often as you need to during a call, without fear of cutting the other person off.

"Now you can explore your contacts at leisure without fear of disconnecting the call, and access the info you desire"

Contacts Accessing your contact book

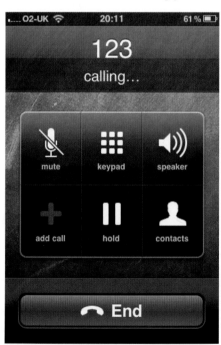

01 Connect a call
To bring up the call menu, you need to dial a number or select a contact. When the other person picks up, the menu will appear. You will find the contacts icon in the bottom right.

02 Bring up contacts
By hitting the contacts icon, you'll go straight to your contact book. From there you can browse your contacts by swiping up and down, or tapping on an entry to see more information.

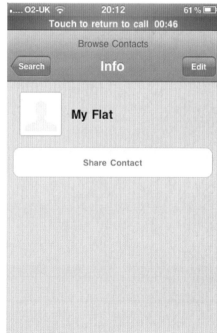

03 Access a contact
Tap a contact to access their info. From there you can see their number and email address. These can be copied and pasted into emails, texts and other apps. Hit the green bar to go back a step.

Make a call from a website

When you're browsing the web and come across a phone number, it's simple to call it straight from Safari

After a while your iPhone can start to feel like the only tool you need to get a lot of tasks done in day-to-day life. Nowadays, when you're looking for a company's number you're just as likely to go online than to the Yellow Pages, and with a browser as good as Safari on the iPhone, it's sure to be the first port of call for many.

Companies now seem much happier dealing with people through the medium of email, but if you want to hear another person's voice, and use your iPhone for its primary function, the device gives you all the tools you need to contact people quickly through the web. When you've found the number you were looking for, you don't need to search for a pen and paper or attempt to memorise the digits – it's a lot simpler than that.

Because both the iPhone and iOS are built entirely by Apple, it has included a number of handy shortcuts to make your life quicker and easier. Apps will work together, switching quickly when you're trying to do something that would work better elsewhere.

This is just the case with phoning people from a website in Safari; if you see a number on a website, tapping it will open up the Phone application, and automatically call the number, saving you a lot of time and hassle. That number will then be stored in your Recent Calls list if you need to get in contact again. When you hang up from your phone call, the Phone app will close, and Safari will be back on your screen, in exactly the same place as you left off. To find out exactly what to do, read on.

Safari Call from a website

01 Find your number

When you've tracked down the number of a company on its website, you should notice it is coloured. This means you can touch it to call the number from the phone app.

02 Touch to call

When you tap on the number, a notification box will pop up asking if you want to call the number. In this case you do, but this stops you calling people when touching the number by accident.

03 You're on call

When you touch Call, you will be transported to the Phone app and the phone will be ringing. When you're finished and have hung up, you will be taken straight back to Safari.

Set a passcode

If you want to feel more secure, setting a passcode on your iPhone will stop anyone else accessing your apps, messages and photos

The iPhone is a very powerful tool, and as you use it more and more, it will contain more and more sensitive information. It might be photos, phone numbers, or apps like Facebook – you won't want anyone else getting your hands on your device. One of the best ways to protect your iPhone is by setting a passcode that is required each time the phone is unlocked. You can switch this option on through the Settings app, and your passcode can be as simple or as complex as you like. In fact, there is a huge amount of customisation on offer in this area, as some people will want a lot more protection than others.

The passcode itself is easy to set up, and soon all your data will be safe from anyone who manages to get to your phone. Each time you unlock your phone by sliding the bar across the screen, a passcode screen will appear and ask for you to input your secret code. You can still make emergency calls from the iPhone, so if for whatever reason you need to quickly call for help you won't need to fumble around trying to remember your code. You can also set the phone to erase all your data if the incorrect code is entered ten times in a row; however this is not something to take lightly, and you should only turn this on in extreme circumstances, when you're sure that you aren't going to forget your code!

"All your data will be safe from anyone who manages to get to your phone"

Settings Turn on passcode lock

01 Find the Menu
The Passcode settings are in the Settings app, under the General tab. If you scroll down you will see this area, with the passcode set to Off as a default. Touch here to set it to on.

02 Choose a code
When you tap the option to turn on a Passcode Lock, you will be asked to input a code of your choice twice. Don't forget this, as you will need it to unlock the phone and change these settings!

03 Unlock your iPhone
When it's set up, and you've changed the settings, you'll see this screen when you unlock your phone. Getting it wrong will bring up a red warning, and you will be asked to try again.

Speed up text entry on your iPhone

The iPhone's touch-screen keyboard splits opinion, but we uncover some hidden gems that might make you a more productive tap-typist

When the iPhone was launched to an expectant public in 2007, without doubt the feature that caused the most heated debate was the touch-screen QWERTY keyboard. Speculation was rife about how users would take to it, and much doubt was cast upon it ever being any use to all but the most nimble-fingered users. Four years and three revisions on, opinion is still divided. Some users have taken to it like a duck to water, while others curse it daily, longing for the feel of physical keys, however tiny, beneath their fingers.

While it cannot be denied that this particular aspect of the iPhone's interface does take some getting used to, there are, in typical Apple style, a number of hidden secrets that may just tip the balance in its favour if you're one of those users who struggle with it on a daily basis. Even if you don't struggle, anything that helps speed up or facilitate text entry on your device can only be a good thing. So here's a round-up of our favourite tips and shortcuts for speeding up text input and minimising frustration when using the iPhone's keyboard.

> ## "Some have taken to it like a duck to water, while others curse it daily"

iOS 4 Text entry tips and shortcuts

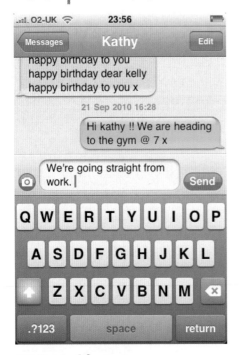

01 Period features

At the end of a sentence, tap the space bar twice to insert a full stop and a space, and automatically start the next sentence with a capital letter. It'll save you a couple of taps immediately.

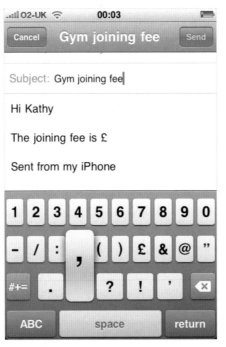

02 Speedy punctuation

Hold the '123' key and slide your finger to the key you want. As you release, the symbol is entered and the keyboard snaps back to the QWERTY layout, saving more precious seconds.

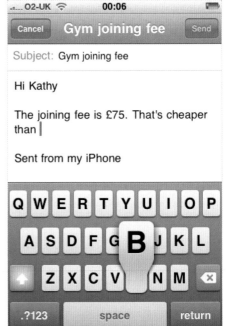

03 Shifty characters

To capitalise individual mid-sentence characters in one keystroke instead of two, hold down the shift key and slide your finger over to the desired letter. It'll then snap back to lower case.

Learn the tricks of text entry

Our top tips for writing text on the iPhone

Shake to undo
To delete what you just typed, a short, sharp left and right shake of the phone will call up an 'Undo Typing' button – a lot more fun than just holding down the backspace key!

Try it out
The easiest way to find out what secret symbols lie beneath which key is to go through the keyboard, holding down keys to see what you get

Landscape artist
If you find that the keys are just too close together, try rotating the phone for a landscape keyboard with wider keys. This works for most apps in which text can be entered

One at a time please
Shortcuts can't be combined – if you access the punctuation layout quickly by holding down the 123 key and sliding across, you won't then be able to hold your finger to produce alternative characters

Knowledge base

On target
Although you wouldn't be able to tell, the iPhone keyboard already helps you out as you type, using a clever predictive algorithm. The software looks at the character you just typed and predicts which key you might go for next. It then invisibly expands the landing area around the most probable target keys, making them easier to hit first time.

04 Vowel play
Holding down most vowel and some punctuation mark keys gives you a pop-up containing alternative international forms of the original character.

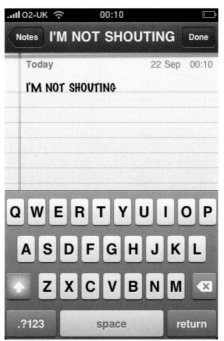

05 Caps lock
For caps lock, go to Settings>General>Keyboard> Enable Caps Lock. Turn this on and a double-tap of Shift turns it blue and puts you in caps lock mode until you toggle it off.

06 Quicker URL entry
When entering website addresses in Safari's URL window, hold down the .com button to reveal a selection of alternative domain options, saving some fiddly typing.

Managing your iPhone messages

Messages are a quick, simple and easy way to communicate. Here we run through the options to keep yours neat, tidy and current

Messages are a staple diet of any modern day smartphone. They are quick, easy, convenient and almost always shorter than a call.

The iPhone follows Apple tradition and adds a little style and panache to the messaging experience. The messages are not simply stored in an inbox, they are stored in conversations, exactly as a user would talk to someone face-to-face. Being colour coded, users can quickly scan a conversation to see the messages received and sent. The integrated copy, paste and replace commands mean that users take even further control of a conversation.

All this works beautifully for almost any exchange of messages, but as a conversation grows it can become unwieldy and sometimes irrelevant. This is where control needs to be passed to the user and as ever the iPhone does it with the greatest degree of functionality. Two taps and the message sender can be called, three taps and a conversation can be deleted. Three taps again and the user gets total control of the individual elements of a conversation – delete or forward, the choice is yours.

"The iPhone follows Apple tradition and adds a little style to the experience"

Messages   Manage and organise iPhone messages

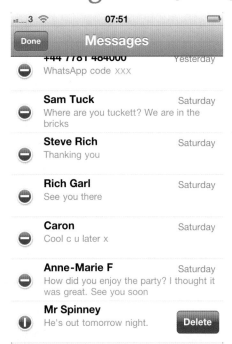

01 View messages

Tap Messages to view the current list of sent messages. To remove a message first tap Edit. Hit the red 'no entry' icon, then the Delete button to get rid of a message.

02 Send a new message

To view a message thread tap the desired message in the list. To send a message hit the box at the bottom, type in a message and then simply tap Send.

03 Copy and paste

To copy text into a new message, tap and hold the appropriate speech bubble and tap Copy. Now tap the message box and hold and tap Paste to add.

Making the most of messaging

Get accustomed to the iPhone's text message interface

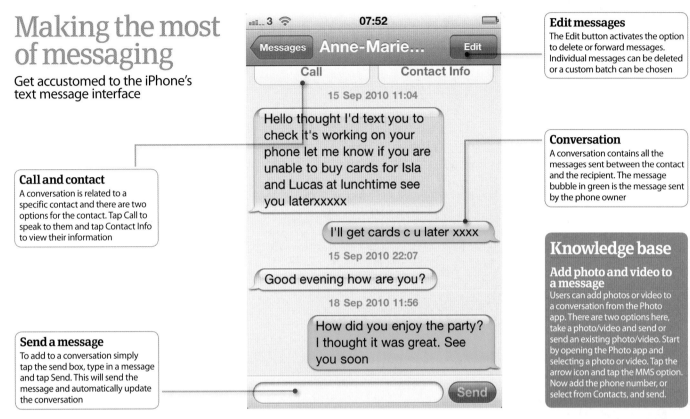

Edit messages
The Edit button activates the option to delete or forward messages. Individual messages can be deleted or a custom batch can be chosen

Conversation
A conversation contains all the messages sent between the contact and the recipient. The message bubble in green is the message sent by the phone owner

Call and contact
A conversation is related to a specific contact and there are two options for the contact. Tap Call to speak to them and tap Contact Info to view their information

Send a message
To add to a conversation simply tap the send box, type in a message and tap Send. This will send the message and automatically update the conversation

Knowledge base

Add photo and video to a message
Users can add photos or video to a conversation from the Photo app. There are two options here, take a photo/video and send or send an existing photo/video. Start by opening the Photo app and selecting a photo or video. Tap the arrow icon and tap the MMS option. Now add the phone number, or select from Contacts, and send.

04 Text options
After pasting in text there is the option to Select, Select All and Paste, as shown in the shot above. Tap Select to choose a word, hit Cut to remove, Copy or Paste.

05 Select individual messages
If a message needs to be removed from a conversation first tap Edit. Each message will now have a radio button. Tap to select the message text.

06 Delete or forward
Selecting messages activates Delete and Forward buttons. Tap Delete to get rid of selected messages, tap Forward to send messages to a new recipient.

Moving icons and using folders

Once you've installed lots of apps, the screens start to fill up and it gets harder to find things. Discover how to organise your apps and keep your iPhone tidy

Whenever a new app is installed, it just gets added to the end of the existing list, or if there's a gap anywhere, it can appear there. This is fine when you only have a handful of apps, but after a couple of months with your iPhone, the screens start to fill up and it all looks disorganised and messy. Fortunately it can all be organised into areas of similar functions, such as games on one page, utilities on another and reference apps on a page as well. You can reorganise your iPhone screens using iTunes, where it is easy to create extra screens, even if the current ones are full, but it's also possible to move icons around directly on the iPhone. Also, you can create as many folders as you like and bundle apps together to make your display very neat and tidy. Final benefits are that unwanted apps can be deleted and must-have apps can be added to the favourites bar at the bottom of every screen.

> "You can create as many folders as you like and bundle apps together to make your display neat and tidy, and must-have apps can be added to the favourites bar"

iPhone Home Keep your iPhone organised

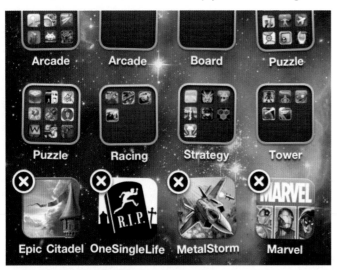

01 Activate the wiggle

Turn your iPhone on so that you are looking at your Home screen. If you have lots of apps then the icons for them will be spread over subsequent screens. To arrange them together tap and hold an app you want to move until all the apps start to wiggle.

02 Move the app

Still holding down on the app, drag your finger to the edge of the screen you want to move to. The apps will scroll sideways to give you the next screen. Move your finger over the place you want the app to go and then let go of it.

Inside the new folder display

How to edit the folder name and move and delete apps inside it

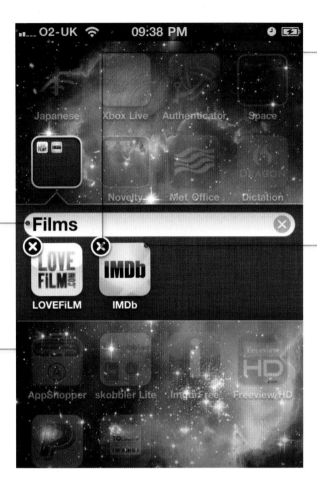

Edit the folder name
Tap a folder to open it. Tap and hold an app inside to go into wiggle editing mode. You can now remove or change the folder name

Take an app out
While in wiggle mode you can drag an app out of the folder again simply by tapping and holding and then moving outside the folder area

Delete an app in a folder
To remove an app that is inside a folder simply tap on the X gadget on the top-left corner. You will still have a backup inside iTunes

Rearrange apps inside the folder
If there's lots of apps inside a folder, rearrange them by tapping and holding and then dragging to a new position. The other apps will shuffle along and move

Knowledge base

Favourite and unwanted apps
When in wiggle mode a little cross appears on the top-left corner of all the apps. Tap on this to delete the app directly from your iPhone. You can't delete the ones the iPhone comes with. The favourites bar at the bottom of the screen comes with four slots for your favourite apps. Again, in wiggle mode you can move them around, drag them on or off the bar or simply add your new, favourite app to the ones there by dragging and releasing the app over it.

03 Create folders for common apps
Press the Home button to exit wiggle mode. To create folders though, drop an app over the top of one you want it to appear in a folder with. A folder is then instantly created with a name that reflects the type of apps if they are fairly similar.

04 Rename the folder
If the folder name isn't to your liking, simply tap on the X gadget to delete it and tap in the text field to enter your own. When complete, press the Home button twice to exit. To add more apps to the same folder, simply drag and drop them into it.

Work with multiple pages in Safari

Browsing the web on the iPhone is completely different to doing so on your Mac or PC. This being an Apple device, though, it's very intuitive…

When Apple revealed the iPhone back in January 2007, it introduced the general public to the notion of holding the internet in your hands and manipulating it simply with your fingers. In one fell swoop, the idea of creating a simplified internet for mobile devices because they supposedly couldn't handle 'proper' webpages was destroyed forever, and the revolution began.

In this tutorial, we will introduce you to the basics of Safari and having multiple windows open at the same time, giving immediate access to all your favourite sites. The principle is the same as managing tabs on your desktop web browser, but with a visually slick, touch-based twist that you would expect from iOS. So grab your iPhone and let's get started navigating those webpages.

> "In one fell swoop, the idea of creating a simplified internet for mobile devices because they supposedly couldn't handle 'proper' webpages was destroyed forever"

Mobile Safari   Open multiple pages in Safari

01 Launch Safari

Tap on the Safari icon to open it and launch a webpage. You'll notice that the address and Google bar are at the top while navigation controls are found at the bottom. For the purposes of this tutorial, the bottom bar is where we'll be focusing our attention.

02 Multiple thumbnails

Tap on the multiple-page icon, which is on the far right at the bottom of the screen, to reveal a new part of the interface. If this is the first time you've done this, you'll notice a smaller thumbnail of your existing page and a button at the bottom called 'New Page'.

Web navigation
Getting to know the functions

URL
This displays the URL of the site you will be opening, or copying

Bookmark bar
This Bookmark bar is only revealed when either the address field or Google search field is selected and the keyboard is up. Hide the keyboard and the bar disappears as well

Copy an address
Use this button to copy a link to the clipboard, ready to be pasted into an email or other app for archiving or to send to someone else

Open a new page
Tap and hold on a link to reveal a pop-up menu from which you can choose to open that link as a new page, preserving the existing one

Knowledge base
Import Bookmarks from your Mac
There are two ways to make sure all the bookmarks you've accumulated on your Mac can be transferred to your iPhone. One of these is through MobileMe: make sure you've ticked 'Bookmarks' in the System Preferences MobileMe Sync tab. If you don't have a MobileMe account, you can do this via iTunes once your iPhone is connected to it.

03 A new page
Tap on that 'New Page' button to open one up, blank and ready to be directed wherever you want it to go, with your other page safe and sound for now. Perform a search, access one of your bookmarks or type in the new address yourself to get going.

04 Limited numbers
There's a limit to the number of pages you can have open at any one time: eight. Once you've hit that number, you'll have to start deleting existing ones if you need to open others, which is done by tapping on the 'x' widget in the top left of a thumbnail.

Getting the most from bookmarks

The iPhone has many uses, but one of its main strengths is browsing the web. Here's how to get the most out of it

The iPhone is great for many things and the extra applications available for it expand its usability even further. Some of the built-in applications will get more use than anything you download from the App Store, however. One of the apps you're likely to use more often than any other is Safari.

Though there are fewer features on the iPhone version of Safari compared to the desktop, there's still a lot you can do with the application. Holding the internet in your hands is great and really changes the way you browse and interact with the web. Though Safari shares its name with the Mac and PC equivalents, it's not exactly the same as those applications. The iPhone version of Safari has been tweaked to work much better with the touch interface. Those of you with MobileMe accounts can also sync their bookmarks with the iPhone and Safari on your computer. You can also add sites to your Home screen for easier access. Here we'll show you how to maximise Safari's bookmark potential.

"iPhone Safari has been tweaked to work with the touch interface"

Synced
Your synced bookmarks from your computer appear in the Bookmarks Bar and Bookmarks Folder directories

Edit
Any edits to your bookmarks will be synced back to your computer when you connect your iPhone to iTunes, or over the air if you're on MobileMe

Safari for iPhone
Get to grips with bookmarks in Safari on the iPhone

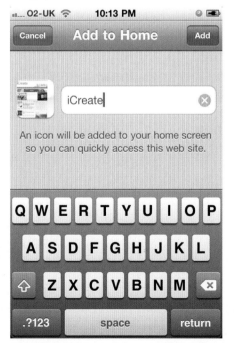

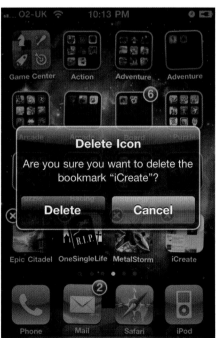

01 Add a website
Navigate to the website you want on your Home screen. When it has loaded tap on the middle icon on the bottom bar and tap Add to Home Screen.

02 Give your icon a name
When you tap on Add to Home Screen it will add the title of the page, but you can edit this to something more appropriate. Tap Add when you're done.

03 Get rid of a home screen icon
If you're not using your bookmarked Home screen icon very much, it's easy to get rid of it. Tap and hold until the x appears at the top right and tap that.

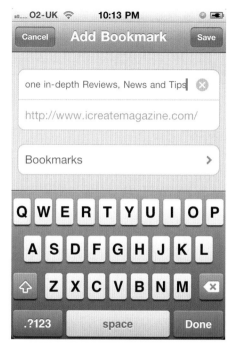

04 Add a bookmark
You'll be familiar with internet bookmarks and you can add them on the iPad too. Tap the same button on the toolbar and then Add bookmark.

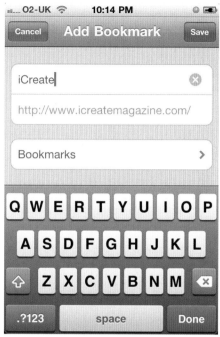

05 Name your bookmark
After you've tapped on Add bookmark you'll have to give your new bookmark a name. This will be automatically chosen, but you can easily change it.

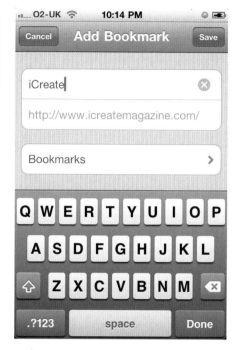

06 Get to your bookmarks
To see your bookmarks, tap on the icon to the right of the middle button. They will be listed under the History and Bookmarks Menu and Bar folders.

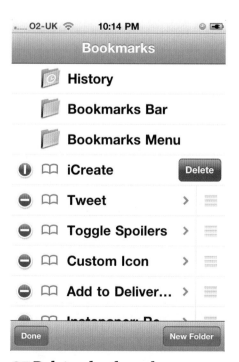

07 Delete a bookmark
To remove a bookmark tap on the bookmarks icon and then tap on Edit. A red icon with a – symbol will appear; tap it and then tap Delete.

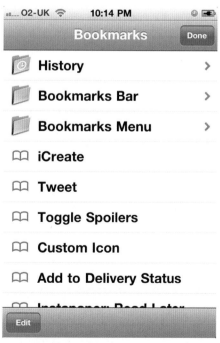

08 Move the bookmark
If you'd like to move a bookmark, tap Edit and then tap on your bookmark. Choose a folder in the field below the address.

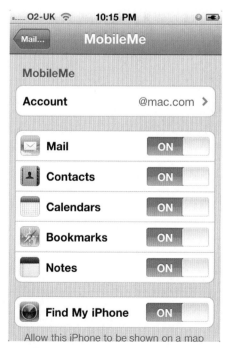

09 MobileMe not syncing?
If you've got MobileMe and it's not syncing, head into the Mail settings, tap your MobileMe account, and ensure that bookmarks are toggled on.

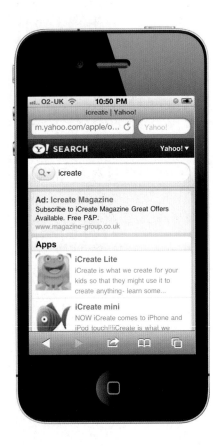

Change the default search engine

The built-in search bar in Safari lets you seek out what you need fast, but you don't have to just use Google to provide your answers – Yahoo! and Bing are options too

When you're searching the web it's probably second nature to just tap on the toolbar and type out your enquiry. By default Apple has chosen to use Google as the search engine of choice and for many people this will be absolutely fine.

However, Google isn't to everyone's tastes so there's the option to swap to Yahoo! or Bing. As it stands, if you use Safari for your web browsing these are your only choices and you can't even pick your favourite location. For instance, you can't set UK as

the location for your preferred results. Some of the third-party web browsers available on the App Store will let you choose from a wider range of default search partners.

Otherwise you can, of course, navigate to the homepage of your favourite search engine and set it as an icon on your home screen. This way you'll always start a new browsing session at your desired search engine. However, for the built-in search bar in Safari you're stuck with just the three until Steve Jobs decides that more are needed.

> "Apple has chosen to use Google as the search engine of choice, but it isn't to everyone's tastes"

Safari on iPhone   Swap default search providers on your iPhone

01 Safari search

If you open Safari you'll see the search bar up in the top-right of the screen. In it will be the name of the current default search engine provider; for example in the screenshot above it's Google. When you begin typing the name disappears.

02 Settings

You can't change the search provider within Safari; instead you have to do it from within the Settings app. You need to press the Home button to quit the app and navigate back to your Home screen. Find the Settings app and then tap on it.

Search engine selection

Find the perfect search engine for you

Search bar
The search bar in Safari can use either Google, Yahoo! or Bing. You can swap between them but sadly you can't choose another provider if you prefer the competition

Suggested results
Both Yahoo! and Google offer suggestions based on what you type, that way you don't always have to type the search term fully. Simply tap on the suggestion to immediately see the associated results appear

Search
When you tap into the search bar the on-screen keyboard pops up automatically. Cleverly, the Return key is swapped for the search command so simply hit that to get the results you want

Knowledge base

Third-party browsers
You don't have to use Safari on the iPhone as there are a number of alternative browsers available on the App Store. These offer more in the way of functionality too, such as tabbed browsing and a larger range of search provider options. Simply type 'web browser' into the App Store search bar and download a selection; some are free, others available for a small fee.

03 Safari settings

In the Settings app you need to scroll down until you find Safari. By tapping on it you will reveal the options that are available to you. Tap on the Search Engine category up at the very top of the settings, listed under General.

04 Make your selection

The scarcity of options here and size given over to show them off would seem to imply that more search engine options could be accommodated. As it stands, however, you have just the three to choose from. Tap on Google, Yahoo!, or Bing and return to Safari.

Organising emails

The Mail app on the iPhone sets a new standard on how emails are managed from touch-enabled devices. In this tutorial we show you how to manage your email

Email is part of everybody's day-to-day life, particularly in the business world. Most of us start our morning with it. Before, checking for emails would mean starting your fully fledged computer, but with the introduction of the iPhone this habit changed drastically. The iPhone provides the best email experience between the mobile devices.

The Mail app supports most of the current generation technology such as automatic service discovery, Exchange for business networks, POP and IMAP for your own hosted or ISP-provided mail and most other mail providers without native support, and a number of dedicated third-party services such as MobileMe, Gmail, Yahoo! Mail and AOL. The Mail app on the iPhone also plays well with other related apps on the iPhone, such as the Calendar, letting you send and receive appointments and import them directly into your itinerary.

In this tutorial we will look into doing a few of the more important tasks using the Mail app. It's all very easy, so let us show you how to manage your emails on the move.

> "Before, checking for emails would mean starting your computer, but with the introduction of the iPhone this habit changed drastically"

Mail Organising emails

01 Adding an email account

Open Settings and select 'Mail, Contacts, Calendars'. You will now be presented with account types that you can use. Tapping on any one of the supported services will open the form asking for account details. Fill in the required information to set up your email account.

02 Searching for emails

Search for emails in Mail by typing onto the Search Box and selecting the From, To or Subject fields. Do a full text search by tapping All. By default this will only do a search on the emails that have been downloaded on the iPhone. To do a full search you can tap on 'Continue Search on Server...'

You've got mail!

Working your way around
the Mail app

Move message
This enables you to move a message to a folder (or mailbox)

Search box
This allows you to search your emails to find a specific one

Refresh mailbox
This checks the mail server for any new messages and downloads them if they are available

Knowledge base

Email Protocols

The iPhone's Mail app supports all major email protocols. These are:

1. Exchange ActiveSync: Exchange ActiveSync is a data synchronisation protocol that provides push synchronisation of emails, tasks, contacts between ActiveSync enabled devices and servers such as the iPhone.

2. IMAP (Internet Message Access Protocol): IMAP is a protocol for retrieving emails and working with mailboxes on a mail server using an email client. Email clients using IMAP generally leave messages on the server until the user explicitly deletes them. This and other characteristics of IMAP operation allow multiple clients to manage the same mailbox.

3. POP (Post Office Protocol): POP is similar to IMAP but does not provide support for using multiple clients using the same mailbox.

03 Moving messages between folders (mailboxes)

Tap Edit, then select all the messages that you want to move to a different folder, then tap Move. Tapping Move will give you a list of the folders that are available; all you need to do is simply tap on a folder to move the selected messages.

04 Tweak the settings

You can configure a wide range of settings which control how Mail works. To access the settings for Mail, tap Settings (from the Home screen), then 'Mail, Contacts, Calendars'. You can change the Account Settings, Mail, Default Account, Signature and more.

How to work with attachments

The iPhone is particularly useful for emailing documents while on the move. Here's how to deal with attachments

I t's hard to imagine a working day when you don't have to deal with email attachments, and it's likely you're going to be faced with similar tasks while on your iPhone. So, how does the iPhone handle these? That question will depend on what's attached to your email in the first place.

This step-by-step tutorial will show you how you can work with your iPhone to handle common files like photos, iWork or Microsoft Office documents and PDFs. They each behave in slightly different ways but the principle is actually very similar and it will take you next to no time to find your way around the iPhone interface.

But receiving attachments is only half the story. It's obvious that you'll also need to send them out too, which is why we'll cover that part as well. So pick up your iPhone and let's see how all of this works.

"You can use your iPhone to handle common files like photos, Office documents and PDFs"

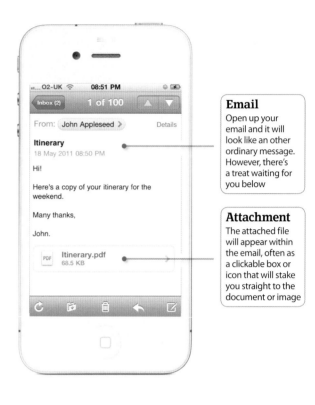

Email
Open up your email and it will look like an other ordinary message. However, there's a treat waiting for you below

Attachment
The attached file will appear within the email, often as a clickable box or icon that will stake you straight to the document or image

Mail Send and receive email attachments

01 Into the Photo app
When you're sent an image, adding it to your photo library is easy: tap and hold on it to reveal a menu. Select Save Image.

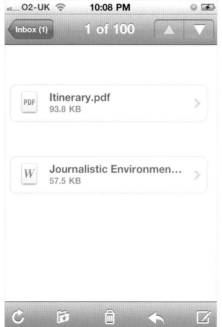

02 RTF and PDF files
If you're dealing with RTF files or PDFs, tapping on its icon will open it in Quick Look, where you can view and copy text, but you can't edit anything.

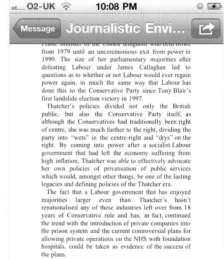

03 iWork and Office documents
With other documents like Word or Pages, tapping on it will lead to the same Quick Look section, but if you need to edit it, there's another way.

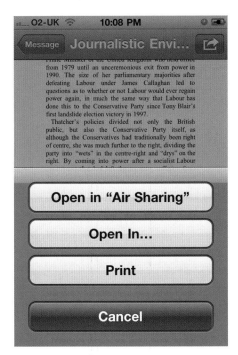

04 Getting out of Quick Look

To get out of Quick Look, tap on Message to get back to Mail, or the attachment can be opened in a supported third-party app. Do the former.

05 Open in an editing app

To get straight to an app without going into Quick Look, tap and hold on the file's icon. This reveals a menu where you can choose to open it in an app.

06 Copying a photo

Going back to a photo attachment, if you want to use it in another app but not add it to your library, tap and hold on it, and select Copy from the menu.

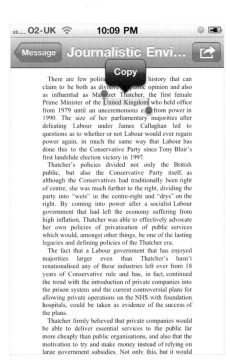

07 Pasting elsewhere

Quick Look may not be able to edit documents, but text and elements can be selected and copied into other apps.

08 Attaching a file

Many text editors, including Notes, feature the ability to attach files to an email. In Notes' case, it's this icon at the bottom.

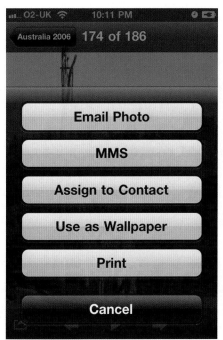

09 Attaching a photo

To send a photo, select it and tap on the sharing button in the bottom left of the Photos app. Send a smaller version when prompted to save time.

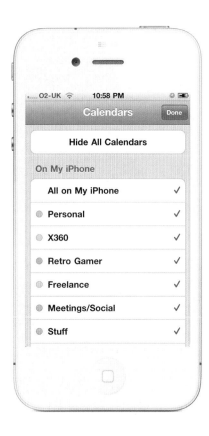

Set the default calendar

The iPhone can handle multiple calendars so you can keep your work, home or family events separate, but you may use one more than another. Here we show you how to set the default

One of the main advantages of the iPhone as an appointment manager is its ability to manage multiple calendars in one very simple interface. You can mix and match your home and work commitments and keep them all in the same place. The colour-coded calendars mean you can know instantly whether the next date in your diary is home, work, or anything else related.

When you're making entries to Calendar on your iPhone it selects a default calendar to store the event in. This is great if the default calendar matches the one you use most. However, if you're using it for mainly work-related stuff and the default calendar is for home, you'll have to change it each time you add an event. You can edit the entries to match the calendar after, but this is a time-consuming process.

Changing the default calendar will make entering new appointments that bit faster and cut down on mislabelled entries too. Of course, the time saved is minimal, but it's one less thing to worry about and will help to keep you more organised in the long run.

> "Colour-coded calendars mean you can know instantly whether the next date in your diary is home, work, or anything else related"

Calendar Change the default calendar

01 Go to Settings

A few of the iPhone's application settings are editable from within the app itself, but in this case you need to go to Settings. Press the Home button and then swipe to the Home screen with the Settings app on it. Simply tap it to open.

02 Mail, Contacts, Calendars

Find Mail, Contacts, Calendars in the Settings app and tap it – it's just below the General settings, marked by the Mail app's icon. This is where the Default Calendar settings are hidden away, right at the very bottom of this menu.

Defining the default calendar

Keeping you in the right place at the right time

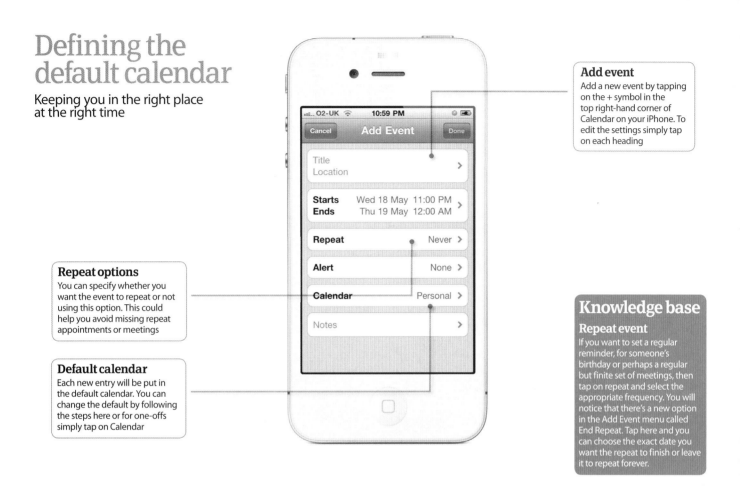

Add event
Add a new event by tapping on the + symbol in the top right-hand corner of Calendar on your iPhone. To edit the settings simply tap on each heading

Repeat options
You can specify whether you want the event to repeat or not using this option. This could help you avoid missing repeat appointments or meetings

Default calendar
Each new entry will be put in the default calendar. You can change the default by following the steps here or for one-offs simply tap on Calendar

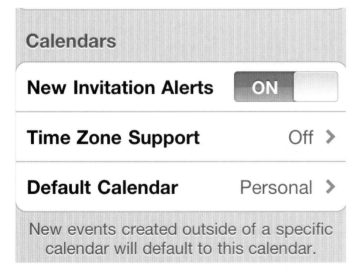

03 Default Calendar

You will need to scroll down by swiping to get to the Default Calendar setting as it is right at the bottom of the page. In the Calendars section the current default calendar will be showing; you can tap on it to access further options that are available.

04 Select your calendar

Here you have a list of all the calendars that are available to you and the currently selected default has a tick next to it. Simply tap on the calendar you would like to select as the new default. Press the Home key when you're done.

Add an Event in your Calendar

Make sure you never miss an important event with Calendar on your iPhone

The Calendar app on the iPhone is pretty useful and very easy to use. Of course, this digital calendar has a multitude of advantages over a real one. Firstly, you get the beauty of typeface rather than scrawled handwriting; secondly, there's no need for Tipp-Ex; and thirdly, you can list your appointments in a number of different ways – list, day or month views are available – to make everything easy to take in. We could go on and on.

Like all the iPhone apps, the Calendar app is easy to use. So easy to use that you'll want to document every move you make using it, from eating breakfast to scheduling toilet breaks. Adding an event is simplicity itself, and your events will sync with iCal on a Mac or Outlook on a PC whenever you connect up your iPhone.

> "Calendar is so easy to use that you'll want to document every move you make using it"

Alert
Notifications are synced with iCal or Outlook on your desktop, so you'll be reminded there as well

Notes
Any important information that doesn't fit anywhere else can be saved as a note in the bottom field

Calendar Add an event

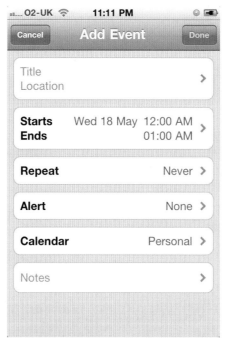

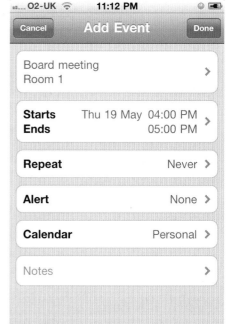

01 Open the app
Open the Calendar app and navigate to the day you want. Presumably you want to add an event, so tap the plus button on the top right.

02 Add event
This menu appears, where you can edit all the details of the new event. Tap the field you wish to edit and then name your event.

03 Detail
You can add as much or as little detail as you want, including the location. You have access to a full keyboard so you can go to town.

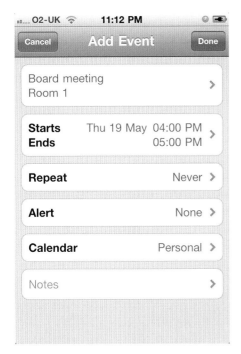

04 Time it

You now need to add the start and end date of your event. Tap on the relevant field to see the time and date menu.

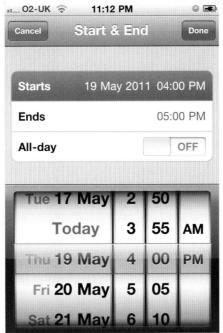

05 Familiar wheels

Use the wheels to select the times and dates that you want to use. You can also toggle the All-day button instead if you wish.

06 Done it

When you have everything in place, you need to tap the Done button. Alternatively you can cancel it to return without saving.

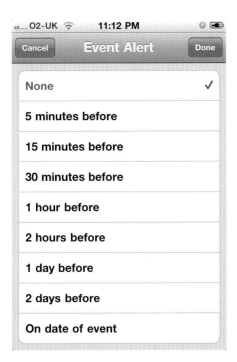

07 Alert

Tap the Alert field to set reminders for the event. These will pop up on your iPhone at the times you set them. There are plenty of options.

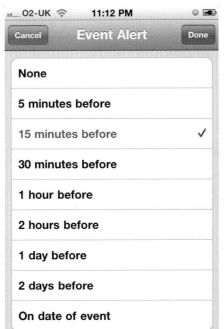

08 Tap it, save it

Tap on the option you wish to use and a tick will appear. Save your progress by tapping the Done button on the top right.

09 Save and view

Save your event and then it will appear on the page. Tap on it to see the full details and tap Edit to make changes or delete the event.

Add a contact

Update your contacts on the iPhone

Now that you've finally got your hands on a shiny new iPhone, one of the first things you're going to want to do is add a contact to the sumptuous Contacts app. It has easy-to-find buttons and an intuitive, natural feel, and if you're new to the whole touch concept then this process will be a revelation in simplicity. Not only can you add all the pertinent information you need but there are cool little extras that make the system very slick and easy to use.

The Contacts app works when your iPhone is held vertically, and this will give you access to all the options you'll ever need. You can literally feel your way around all of the apps on the iPhone, and the Contacts app is certainly no different. Remember that even if you make a mistake you can go back and edit anything you like over and over again until you're happy with it. You can also sync existing contacts from iTunes into the app, which is handy if you've already gone to the effort of creating your contacts on your desktop.

"You can literally feel your way around all of the apps on the iPhone, and the Contacts app is no different"

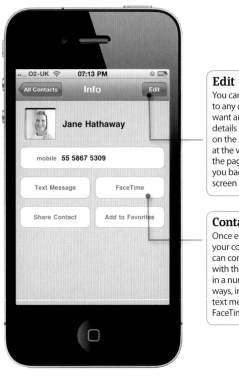

Edit
You can go back to any contact you want and edit their details by tapping on the Edit button at the very top of the page. It will take you back to the screen in step two

Contact
Once entered into your contacts, you can communicate with the person in a number of ways, including text message and FaceTime

Contacts Add a people to your contacts

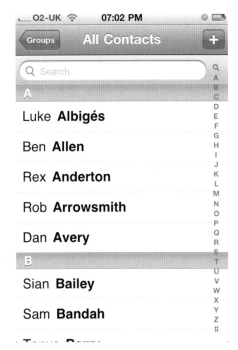

01 Open her up
Open the Contacts app from the Home screen of your iPhone and then use the '+' button, which can be found in the top right-hand corner.

02 Tap and type
You can begin entering the necessary information. Tap on the field you wish to edit. A logical place to start is with the first name.

03 Cross it
As you get used to the keyboard you may make mistakes. You can use the backspace button to delete or remove everything using the little cross.

04 Add a photo

To add a photo just tap the add photo button and you can either take a photo or add one from your photo library.

05 Take your pic

You can now choose from the pictures you have to hand. If there are more pictures than can fit in the window then you can scroll up and down.

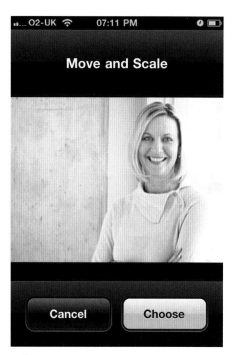

06 Move and scale

You now have to move and scale the picture you have selected. Use a pinch or reverse pinch to zoom in and out of the picture.

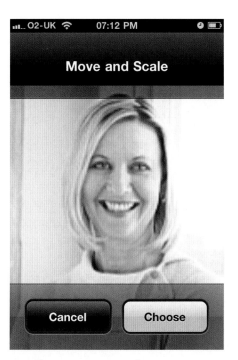

07 Choose or cancel

Once the picture is how you would like it tap on the Choose button at the bottom of the window. The picture you have selected will slide into place.

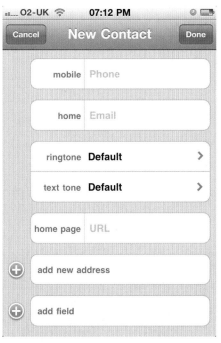

08 Add fields

Go through the rest of the form and add as much or as little information as you need. Just tap into a field to edit it and the keyboard will spring up.

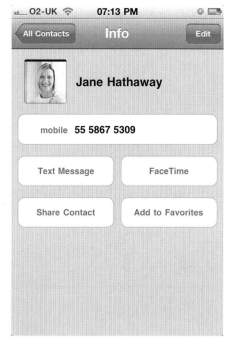

09 Done

Once you are completely finished all you need to do is hit the Done button in the top-right of the page to save the changes.

Create, send and receive contacts

Contacts on the iPhone is a feature-rich contact management system. We'll show you how to create, send and receive contacts

As discussed on the previous page, contacts on the iPhone are managed using a built-in app called **Contacts**. It provides easy access to all your contacts without needing an address book or a PC. It also allows you to store information for each contact, such as address, birthday, notes etc. But it is much more than just that, as Contacts is integrated with other apps, such as Maps and Mail. You can use the Maps app to show a contact's location, the same way you can also add an address to a contact.

Contacts allows you to sync with a variety of services, such as Google Contacts, Yahoo! Address Book, MobileMe, Microsoft Exchange Server and LDAP (Lightweight Directory Access Protocol) Server. Contacts makes it very easy to search for the contact information. If you have a Microsoft Exchange account on your iPhone, you may also be able to search your enterprise Global Address List (GAL) for contacts in your organisation. But one of the most prominent features of Contacts is sharing. Sharing allows you send a contact in vCard (.vcf) format using email. Similarly, you can receive a shared contact as a vCard attachment in Mail. We will look into creating, syncing, sending and receiving contacts.

"The iPhone provides easy access to all your contacts without needing an address book or a PC"

Contacts Learn your way around the Contacts app

01 Create a contact

As discussed on the previous page, it is very simple to add contacts. To recap: open Contacts, tap '+' to open the New Contact form and enter the details. You can tap 'Add new address' to add an address to the contact and tap 'Add field' to add additional fields. Tap Done to save the new contact.

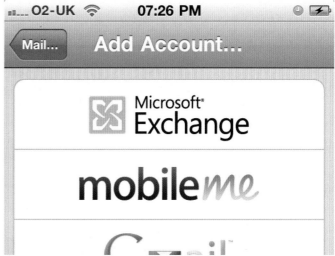

02 Add contacts via syncing

You can also add contacts another way. Syncing Contacts allows you to access your contacts from other locations and services. To do this, you can use iTunes to sync Address Book contacts on your PC or Mac or use your iPhone to add a Microsoft Exchange Server, MobileMe, or LDAP server.

Use the iPhone's Contacts app

Search, share and edit your contacts

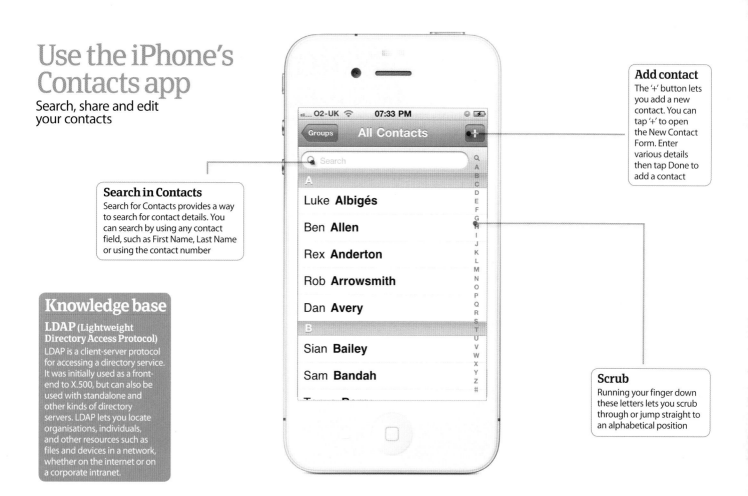

Search in Contacts
Search for Contacts provides a way to search for contact details. You can search by using any contact field, such as First Name, Last Name or using the contact number

Add contact
The '+' button lets you add a new contact. You can tap '+' to open the New Contact Form. Enter various details then tap Done to add a contact

Scrub
Running your finger down these letters lets you scrub through or jump straight to an alphabetical position

Knowledge base

LDAP (Lightweight Directory Access Protocol)
LDAP is a client-server protocol for accessing a directory service. It was initially used as a front-end to X.500, but can also be used with standalone and other kinds of directory servers. LDAP lets you locate organisations, individuals, and other resources such as files and devices in a network, whether on the internet or on a corporate intranet.

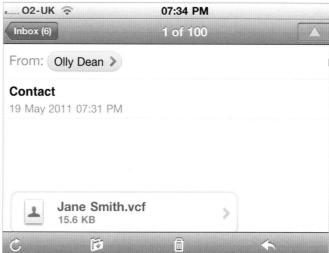

03 Sending a contact

To send a contact, open the contact you want to send then tap Share Contact. You will be given the option to send it in an email or direct to a phone as an MMS (multimedia message). vCard is a universal standard, so it doesn't only work on iPhones.

04 Receive a contact

On the iPhone you can receive a shared contact as a vCard (.vcf) attachment inside an email. Open the email with the contact and tap the '.vcf' file to open the contact details. Tap 'Create New Contact', or 'Add to Existing Contact' to save the information into an existing contact.

Using Notes on iPhone

Don't feel you need to purchase a word processor in order to jot down ideas on your iPhone – you can do this with Notes

Despite the fact that some people view the iPhone as simply a phone and a device that has been designed to consume media, just spending a few minutes with it will make you realise that this is complete nonsense and there's a lot more to it. With the help of a few choice programs, the iPhone is very capable of being used to create drawings, edit photos or even write essays.

But you actually don't need to purchase anything for the latter, as the Notes app comes bundled with the iPhone and is a really great place to start exploring how you can handle typing on glass. You may find it a lot easier than you think, and this built-in app can actually handle a variety of different tasks. What's more, if you're on a Mac your notes will sync directly into Mail, so transferring your notes to your computer is completely effortless.

This step-by-step tutorial will show you how it works, what you can do with it, and how it could help you in your day-to-day activities… it's much more useful than you may think…

> "The Notes app comes bundled with the iPhone and is a really great place to start exploring how you can handle typing on glass"

Notes Use Notes to write down ideas

01 The look of Notes
Hold your iPhone in the portrait orientation and tap the Notes app. The keyboard will appear automatically and you can begin typing.

02 The '+' button
When you've finished, tap Done. When you've finished looking at your note, tap the '+' button in the top-right corner.

03 From one to another
That last action created a new note. You can swap between the first one and the one you're working on by tapping on the arrow buttons.

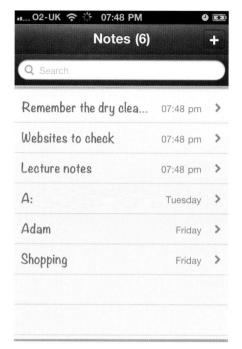

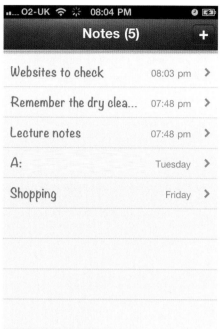

04 Note list

If you want to see all the pages you've created, tap on the Notes button. They're presented in the order you last edited them.

05 See them all

The last-edited note is at the top of the list. If you have more notes than can fit on a single screen, you can scroll down to see them all.

06 Searching

There's also a search field at the top of the list, which can help you narrow down your search when you're looking for specific information.

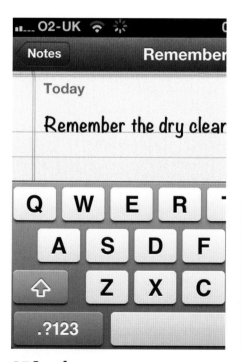

07 Landscape

Turn the iPhone to the landscape orientation. This way you can get a slightly less cramped keyboard, which you may find more comfortable.

08 Tappable links

If you type in a web link, it'll become active. Tap on it and you'll be sent to Safari. Tapping an email address sends you to Mail.

09 Save numbers

The iPhone also recognises phone numbers. Tap one and you can save it to a new or existing contact, or directly call or text it.

Learn to save a bookmark in Maps

Save your favourite places easily in this app

The Maps app is an incredibly useful addition to the iPhone and one that we have used countless times while we are out and about. Playing around with this app really is pure fun, but that shouldn't detract from the practical side that a huge map at your fingertips can actually have.

With this in mind, it's useful to know how to quickly search for items and save them so that they can be called upon at any time, especially when you're pushed for time. The iPhone Maps app is very simple to use and has some very cool features, and coupled with the built-in assisted GPS hardware on your iPhone, it will become an invaluable navigation tool that – unlike many dedicated GPS solutions – won't cost you a penny to use, since it pulls its data straight from Google's superb mapping service and onto your handset.

> "Playing around with this app really is pure fun, but that shouldn't detract from the practical side that a huge map at your fingertips can have"

Maps Adding a location bookmark

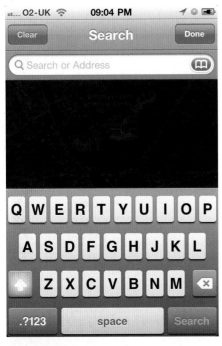

01 Load it, tap it

Load Maps from your Home screen and begin your search by tapping your finger on the address/location field at the top of the interface. Type it in or search for your current location.

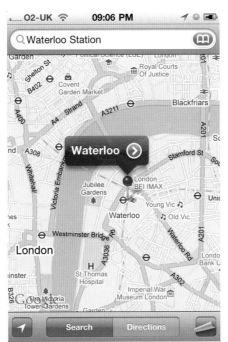

02 Type it, watch it

Once you've typed in your place and hit the search button, a pin will drop in the location. This should happen with satisfying speed. Above the pin the location should be named.

03 View change

You can change the view of the location in question by activating the hidden menu. To do this, tap the button in the bottom-left corner of the screen. Tap on a view option.

Find your way

Maps makes full use of the iPhone's location services to offer navigation information

Start: Current Location

End: Waterloo

Waterloo

Search Directions

My location, different location

The 'My Location' button is situated at the bottom of the screen. Tap it to have your own location triangulated automatically

Cool clarity

The full zoom on the Maps app lets you see the planet in really stunning detail. The speed with which this app can do this only adds to the mesmerising nature of the experience

Toggle it

On the bottom of the interface is the toggle switch between the search function and the directions function, letting you use Maps as a satnav system

Knowledge base

Super speed

The speed of the Maps app comes down to the Apple-made A4 processor and the RAM chip it's connected to working together to make a much snappier experience. The maps render much faster than the iPhone 3GS.

04 Zoom it

Use a pinch or reverse pinch to zoom in and out of the map so you can get an idea of what surrounds the location. You could be looking for nearby tube stations or bus stops, for example.

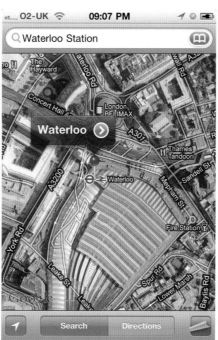

05 Closer look

You can also get in nice and close to your location and see exactly what it looks like. To begin adding it as a bookmark you need to hit the button next to the tag.

06 Save bookmark

The info menu will now open and you can use the button at the bottom to add the location to your Maps bookmarks. This process can be repeated for every location you want to add.

Get directions to a location using Maps

One of the most prominent features of the Maps application is directions. You can get directions between any two locations

The Maps application on the iPhone is superb as a navigation aid when you're out and about in an unfamiliar location.

Maps can be used to get directions between two places. It pulls out a lot of useful information related to a route that is very useful for a commuter, such as Driving/Transit/Walking Directions, Distance and Time to Commute. When using Transit Directions it also shows you the Transit Timings to help you plan ahead. You can also make use of the Traffic information when using directions, which will help you avoid unwanted delays. You can also use Google Street View to get a panoramic view of the destination, but note that this is not available on all the locations. The locations where it is available are indicated by the Street View icon.

In this tutorial we will find the directions between two different towns, proving along the way just how well the Maps app works on the iPhone and how it won't steer you wrong.

> "The built-in Maps application on the iPhone is superb as a navigation aid when you're out and about in an unfamiliar location"

Maps Get directions using Maps

01 Set the Start Address
Search for a location on the map or, if you want to start from the current location, tap the My Location button in the bottom left of the screen. Tap the pin to bring up the menu, and choose Directions From Here. Tap Directions, then enter the address. Now tap Search.

02 Set the destination address
Enter the destination location in the End box. In case there are multiple addresses for the searched address, Maps will put red pins for all the searched locations and set the destination to the one it finds most accurate. You can also select the address if it has already been searched previously.

Get directions on your iPhone

Use the Maps app to reach your destination

Current location
Locate the current address with the help of any of the available GPS technologies

Bookmarks/ Recents/Contacts
Access Map Bookmarks, Recent Location Searches and Contacts through the Search view

Zoom in
You can focus your attention on a specific area, and then you have the option to drop pins onto the map at locations

Knowledge base

GPS technology on the iPhone

GPS alone is rather slow at triangulating your location, so your iPhone will use it in conjunction with the Skyhook database of Wi-Fi hotspots and your cell location to narrow it down quickly, before GPS eventually gives an accurate location. This technique is known as assisted GPS, or A-GPS.

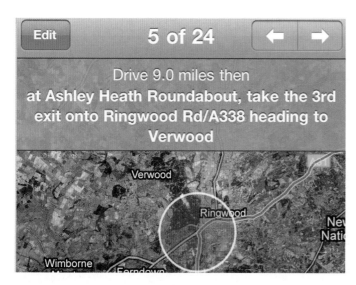

03 Getting the directions

Select the method of commute by tapping one of the icons in the top left-hand corner of the map. The options are for road, public transport or on foot. When a method is selected, tap Start to begin your journey.

04 Arrive

You can navigate through turn-by-turn directions using a swipe of a finger. Directions will indicate turns and distances so you can be sure you get the right one each time. All being well, your iPhone will guide you to your destination in record time.

Send and receive locations with Maps

Maps on the iPhone makes it very easy to share your location

The Maps application on the iOS platform is much more than just a simple map.

It provides a wide range of things to do around maps, such as finding a route, studying geographical information, viewing real-time traffic information, viewing traffic, street views and much more besides.

Among these there is a feature that is exceptionally useful called Share Location. To portray the usefulness of this little feature, let's say that while driving around you have discovered a cave that contains the treasure of Marco Polo. So you think you need to take it all now otherwise somebody else might discover it and take it. What will you do? You will open your iPhone, find out the current location and then send an email with directions to the cave using the Share Location feature, that's what. That way you can get a friend to come and help you with the wealth of goodies contained within.

In this step-by-step tutorial we will show you exactly how to share your location using the Maps app, so that you never miss an opportunity – especially one as big as this. Okay, so this kind of epic event won't happen to you all the time, but there are plenty of other occasions when rather than giving someone convoluted directions, you can just share your location easily using this method. It's really pretty easy, and here we show you how…

"There are plenty of occasions when rather than giving someone directions, you can just share your location easily"

Maps Use the Maps app to let others know where you are

01 Locating the address

To begin, you need to locate the address you want to share. You can do this by searching your location in the search box or by dropping a pin on the location you want to share. A box will appear containing your location on screen.

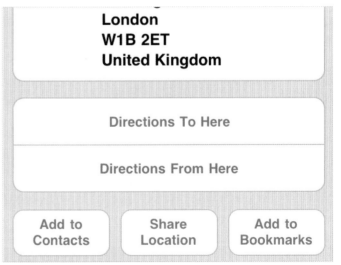

02 Sharing the location

Once you have the correct location, tap on the pin to bring up the detailed information window. Tap the Share Location button available at the bottom of the window (you can also add the address to your contacts or bookmarks from here).

Show friends where you are

Send your current location to friends via email

Pick a Pin
Tap on any pin and you will see an information window which will allow you to share the location with anyone you like

Where it's at
Once you've tapped the current location button your location will appear as a blue dot with a blue ring around it

Map Type
Here we are using a satellite image but you can use a standard map image, or a hybrid that shows satellite imagery overlaid with map info like road names

Knowledge base
VCF file
'.vcf' is the extension of a file used to store electronic business cards in the vCard format. A 'vcf' file may contain name and address info, phone numbers, email addresses, URLs, logos, photos, and audio clips. 'vcf' or vCard format is popular to share contact info on the internet or between devices. Other standards for sharing contact info is hCard and Internet Business Card.

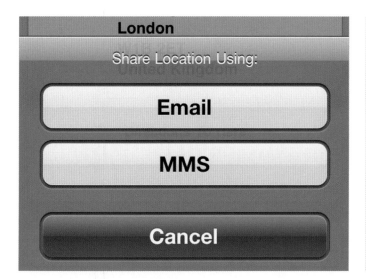

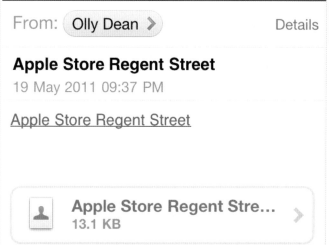

03 Sending the location
Choose whether to share your location over email or MMS. An email is already populated with important information such as the location (in the form of a 'vcf' file) and the location's name as the subject and body. Tap Send to send the location to the recipient.

04 Using the Shared Location
Open the email with the 'vcf' file attached in it. Tap on it to open the information window. It is similar to one you have seen in the Maps application, but it contains more information. It also contains the Map URL. Tap on Map URL to launch the Maps app with the sent address.

Getting started

Access video content via the YouTube app

You don't need us to explain what YouTube is, but it will be useful to know how to get the most out of it on your iPhone. It works using 3G and Wi-Fi

The built-in YouTube iPhone app is a lesson in thoughtful design, and manages to bring the desktop experience to a mobile device while maintaining all of the functionality of the main web portal YouTube uses. With a YouTube account in place you can save favourites, share videos with friends and comment on videos you like, and your changes will be accessible on your desktop automatically. It all sounds very simple and on the whole it is, but some pointers will help you to get even more out of the experience.

It is worth remembering that, should you use the service over 3G, you will be pushing a hefty amount of data so be aware of the limits your network provider has imposed on your account. Wi-Fi is the recommended solution for YouTube

use on an iPhone because it speeds up the loading of videos and also makes the experience feel more like the one you have come to expect on a desktop. The iPhone YouTube app really does bring every feature to your mobile life, and here we will show you how to get up and running in no time and how to make the most of its potential. It's all free so you have no reason not to try it for yourself.

"The YouTube app is a lesson in thoughtful design"

YouTube Make the most of YouTube

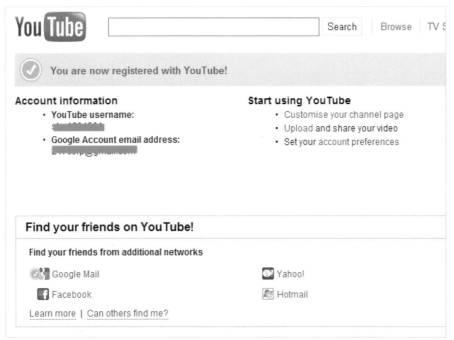

01 Getting started and creating an account

To utilise every feature in YouTube for the iPhone you will need an account. From your desktop computer, go to **www.youtube.com** and click the Create Account option in the top right-hand corner. Complete the requested information and then set up a new Google account (or use your current account in the next page). This completes the process for setting up a new YouTube account.

02 Make YouTube personal

On the iPhone, open the YouTube app and tap Favourites, then tap the Sign In icon, and input your username and password. You will now have access to your videos, favourites and more.

iPhone YouTube

Once you discover how to use YouTube on your iPhone, you may decide to use it as a replacement for the desktop version...

Popular videos
The most recent popular videos of all time, from the past week and from today are a useful way to simply browse and see what's happening on YouTube

Search everything
You can search almost the entire YouTube database from your iPhone in the same way you use a standard web search engine

Previews
Each video is previewed with an icon, rating and the number of views, which together should tell you if it's worth watching

Keep it personal
Your main account information is kept up to date and is accessible via the handy icons at the bottom of each section

Knowledge base
Streaming
Streaming video wirelessly is very bandwidth-hungry, and overuse on 3G alone could cause you to break the limit on your data account. Your network provider is then within its rights to send you a warning. If possible, try to use Wi-Fi because this will not only perform better, but could potentially save you a lot of money.

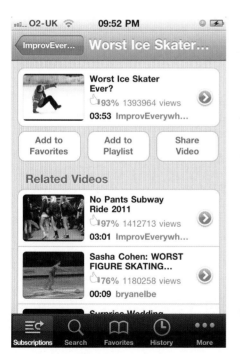

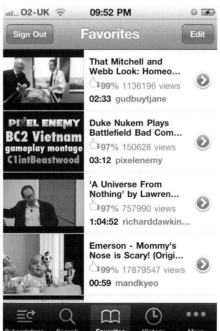

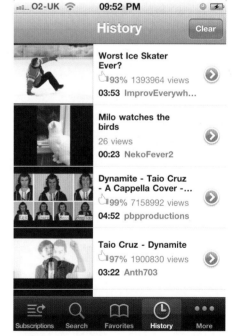

03 Explore the content
You can now explore the content within YouTube. When you tap a video to watch it you will see a selection of buttons on the information page to mark favourites or share videos.

04 Fully in step
Any changes that you make to your YouTube account on the iPhone will be mirrored on your desktop, and vice versa, so you can use both and keep the changes intact.

05 Keep track
YouTube includes a History icon (found along the bottom of the screen) that shows your most recently viewed videos. This is useful if you forget to add a viewed video to your favourites list.

Getting started

Get the most out of iPhone videos

The iPhone is perfectly designed for the mobile movie experience thanks to its high-resolution screen, long battery life and carry-anywhere form. It's time to make the most of it…

The iPhone's video feature alone has the potential to keep you occupied on long plane journeys, in hotels or waiting rooms, and adds a use to the iPhone that could almost justify half of the cost straight away. It has been designed for ease of use, as most Apple software is, and takes care of many of the niggles found in competing devices.

For example, it will automatically play a film or television show from the point you left it, and expanding the screen requires a simple double tap.

Everything is designed to help you get the most from the experience, but some tips are still useful to get you off to a flying start.

In this step-by-step we will show you how to obtain new movies and television programmes, how to transfer them to your iPhone and how to make the most of the viewing experience. You could easily do all of this yourself, but a little knowledge goes a long way and missing out on the movie capabilities of the iPhone would be a real shame given the benefits it offers.

"The video feature adds a use to the iPhone that could almost justify half of the cost straight away"

---

iPhone Videos Make the most of movies and TV shows

01 Grab a film

The easiest way to obtain good quality content is via iTunes. Navigate to the Films or TV Programmes section and choose the film or programme you would like to rent or buy. You can also try some free trailers to get started without spending any money.

02 Put it on the iPhone

The most stable method of moving films to your iPhone is to choose 'Manually manage music and video' in the iPhone summary screen in iTunes. You can then just drag new films over to your iPhone in the left-hand column when you want to.

Watch movies and TV on your iPhone

Get the most out of portable video

Full screen
Tapping on this icon will alternate between full-screen and widescreen viewing. You can also double tap anywhere on screen to achieve this effect

Back where you left off
The iPhone automatically remembers where you finished watching and will start any film at that exact place when you open it up again

Full control
You can move to specific parts of a video by moving the slider at the top with your finger; the further down the screen your finger is, the more precise the movement

Main controls
The main control keys are standard and are brought up by tapping the screen once. You can play, pause, forward or rewind when you need to

Knowledge base
HD
Many iTunes movies and TV programmes are now offered in HD format, which offers a much crisper viewing experience. Sometimes you will pay more for the video, but think of it in a similar way to paying more for Blu-ray. These files will also be larger in size, sometimes significantly, so make sure you have adequate space before you buy.

03 The fun starts here

All you need to do now is simply tap the iPod icon and choose the film or TV show you want to watch from the list of videos that you have installed on your iPhone. The film – or TV programme, for that matter – will immediately start to play from the beginning.

04 Small changes

Double-tapping the screen will make the movie play in full-screen mode, and doing so again will take it back to standard format (which is useful for widescreen films). The rest of the on-screen tweaks are obvious in their implementation, such as play, pause, etc.

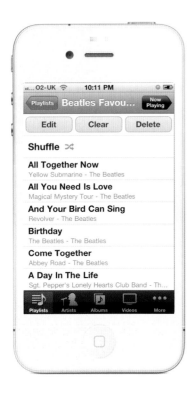

Create a playlist using the iPod app

Manipulate a built-in iPod and have your favourite tracks at your fingertips, wherever you are

With all the bells and whistles that the iPhone has to offer, it's easy to forget that it's also a very impressive iPod. The interface is clean, simple, easy to manipulate and great fun to play with. The familiarity to iTunes doesn't just extent to the app's looks either. The functionality is also pretty similar – the key difference being the way you access and change information. It's all done with a finger and for that reason it feels a thousand times more intimate than using the desktop version, and also makes it much quicker too.

One of the first things you may want to do on the iPhone's iPod is create a playlist. The system Apple has devised for this is really impressive. So impressive, and fun, that you'll want to sift through an entire library and create one playlist after another. Here's how…

"With all the bells and whistles that the iPhone has to offer, it's easy to forget that it's also a very impressive iPod"

iPod Create a playlist

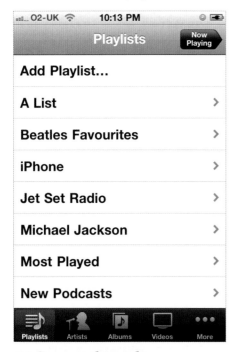

01 Open and tap plus

Open the iPod app on your iPhone. Now tap 'Add Playlist…' at the top of the list of existing playlists on the opening menu to begin creating a brand-new playlist.

02 Type the title

A window appears allowing you to name the playlist. The keyboard automatically springs up from the bottom of the app, allowing you to easily type in a suitable title.

03 Save it

Give your playlist an appropriate name and then tap the Save button. The playlist will then be created in the iPod app and a brand-new screen will appear.

Music while you're mobile

Setting up playlists on the iPhone is a breeze

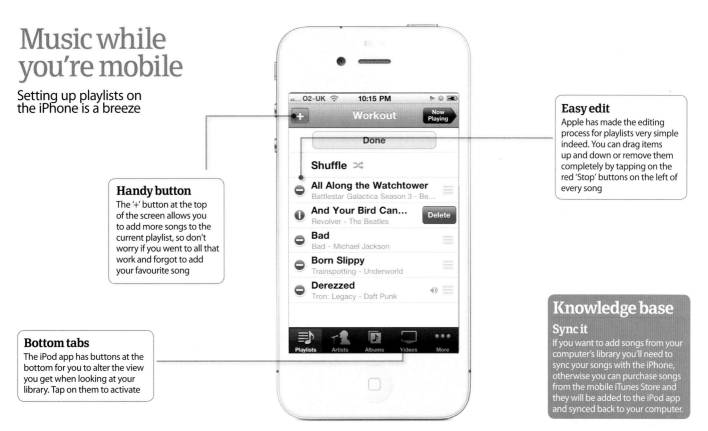

Handy button

The '+' button at the top of the screen allows you to add more songs to the current playlist, so don't worry if you went to all that work and forgot to add your favourite song

Easy edit

Apple has made the editing process for playlists very simple indeed. You can drag items up and down or remove them completely by tapping on the red 'Stop' buttons on the left of every song

Bottom tabs

The iPod app has buttons at the bottom for you to alter the view you get when looking at your library. Tap on them to activate

Knowledge base

Sync it

If you want to add songs from your computer's library you'll need to sync your songs with the iPhone, otherwise you can purchase songs from the mobile iTunes Store and they will be added to the iPod app and synced back to your computer.

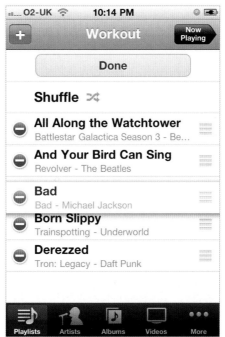

04 Tap it out

Your whole library now appears in the main window and you can tap on each song you wish to appear in the library. Selected items get greyed out so you don't pick them twice.

05 Done, drag, Done

Once you've picked your songs hit Done to see another screen. This time you can drag tunes into the order you want them by dragging up the lined symbol on the right of each song.

06 Play it, love it

When you're completely set on the order that you want, all you have to do is hit the Done button again and your playlist is ready to play and enjoy at your leisure.

Get the most from iTunes

You can download all your favourite movies and music from iTunes without needing to connect it to your computer

Being able to download music and movies on the go is one of the best things about Apple's devices, and this is especially true of the iPhone. With the enormous selection available on the iTunes Store, you're unlikely to be lost for something to suit your mood.

It's not just music and movies though, as you can also download TV programmes, audio books and podcasts. There's even the iTunes U section, which is full of excellent education resources. Coupled with apps like Shazam, you can get the fantastic experience of using your phone to identify a track by listening to it, and then instantly hopping online to buy your own copy.

Your purchases are automatically synced and backed up to your copy of iTunes on your computer whenever you connect the iPhone to it. This means that you'll be able to watch your movies on your computer or Apple TV and, more importantly, that you'll have a guaranteed backup of everything you purchase, just incase you lose your iPhone or you're running out of storage space and have to delete them from your phone.

To use iTunes on the iPhone you will need an account to get going, but once that has been set up you can buy songs, apps or movies wherever you are. All you need is a credit card (or, failing that, some iTunes gift cards).

> "With the enormous selection of music available to download, you're unlikely to be lost for something to suit your mood"

iTunes Make the most of iTunes on the iPhone

01 Buy music, movies and more
To buy music and video from the iTunes Store you'll need to set up an account. Simply tap on an item to buy it and choose Create New Apple ID.

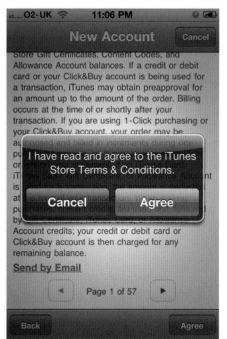

02 Agree to the terms
Once you've confirmed your location you'll then be offered the terms and conditions for using the account. All 57 pages of them!

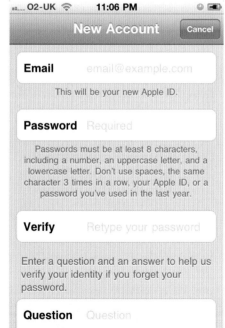

03 Enter your details
You'll need to provide your credit card details. If you don't want to do this, simply buy an iTunes gift card and enter the number here.

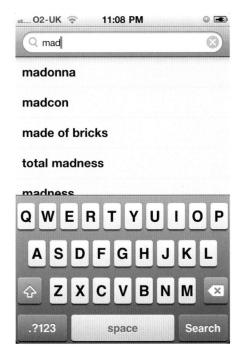

04 Search

To search for your favourite music, video and television programmes, tap the Search button. It will offer suggestions as you type.

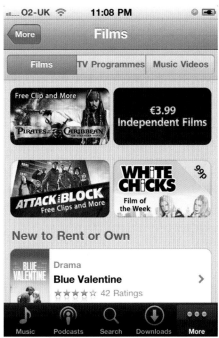

05 Music, Video, TV

To see what's just been added or the latest promotions, just tap on the Video icon along the bottom of the screen.

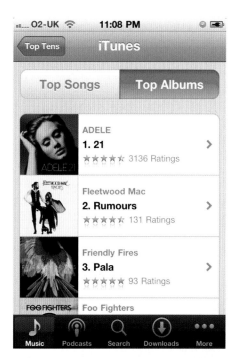

06 Charts

The most popular content in each of the sections is on the Charts page. There are charts pages for everything, including podcasts and TV shows.

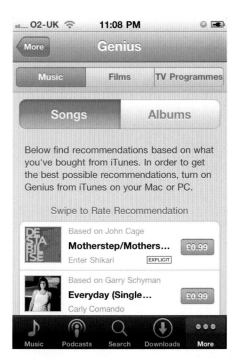

07 Genius

If you have bought from the Store before, tap on the Genius button to see recommendations based on the content of your library.

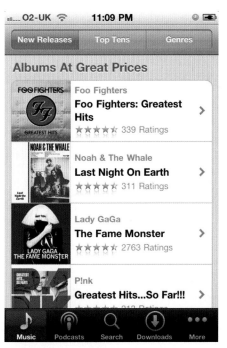

08 Other offers

On the main screen it's easy to be lured in by the flashy graphics, but scroll down and you'll see further offers like free content and cheap music.

09 Monitor downloads

When you've made a purchase, you can see how long it's going to take by tapping on the Downloads icon in the bottom-right corner.

Getting started

Use iTunes to download music to your iPhone

Preview and download your favourite songs from Apple's iTunes Store using your iPhone's iTunes app and then enjoy music on the move!

You could link your iPhone to your desktop computer and transfer your favourite songs onto it via iTunes. However, as you're likely to carry your precious iPhone around wherever you go – hopefully in a soft protective case to keep it in pristine condition – you have the freedom to browse, download and store your favourite music tracks onto it, so that you can listen to them whenever and wherever you fancy, without having to rely on your CD music collection.

You no longer need to be chained to a home computer thanks to the iPhone's own iTunes app.

When you take a fancy to a song that you hear in your local Wi-Fi-enabled coffee shop or over 3G, you can fire up iTunes on the iPhone, search for the song on the iTunes Store and download it there and then to expand your music collection. This is also a great way of downloading just a single song instead of having to purchase the whole album, especially now it seems CD singles are limited to charity records or *X Factor* winners!

You will need to create an account with the iTunes Store before you can buy and download music to your iPhone, though.

> "When you take a fancy to a song, you can fire up iTunes on the iPhone, search for the song and download it there and then"

iTunes Download music from iTunes

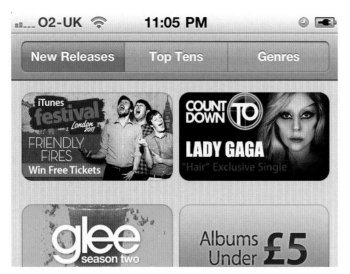

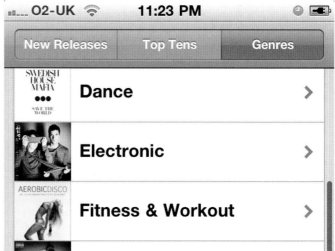

01 Open iTunes

Tap on the iTunes app on your iPhone to launch it. It will take you to the iTunes Store. Tap on the note-shaped Music icon at the bottom left of the page. You'll see thumbnails linking to new and noteworthy music tracks, as well as colourful banners advertising new albums.

02 Choose a genre

To find the type of music you enjoy, tap on Genres at the top of the screen. This lets you fine-tune your browsing to Pop or Electronic music, for example. Tap on a genre to access its page. You will then be taken to a special storefront for your preferred genre.

Get music from iTunes

Browse, preview and download music using iTunes' very easy-to-use interface

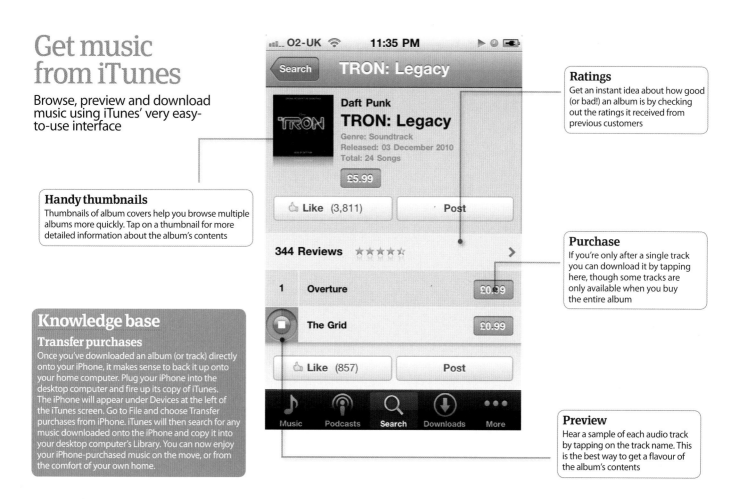

Ratings
Get an instant idea about how good (or bad!) an album is by checking out the ratings it received from previous customers

Handy thumbnails
Thumbnails of album covers help you browse multiple albums more quickly. Tap on a thumbnail for more detailed information about the album's contents

Purchase
If you're only after a single track you can download it by tapping here, though some tracks are only available when you buy the entire album

Preview
Hear a sample of each audio track by tapping on the track name. This is the best way to get a flavour of the album's contents

Knowledge base
Transfer purchases

Once you've downloaded an album (or track) directly onto your iPhone, it makes sense to back it up onto your home computer. Plug your iPhone into the desktop computer and fire up its copy of iTunes. The iPhone will appear under Devices at the left of the iTunes screen. Go to File and choose Transfer purchases from iPhone. iTunes will then search for any music downloaded onto the iPhone and copy it into your desktop computer's Library. You can now enjoy your iPhone-purchased music on the move, or from the comfort of your own home.

03 Preview a track

Tap the Search button at the bottom of the window and enter a term. A variety of thumbnail links will appear. To discover more about a particular album tap on its thumbnail. Tapping a track name will play you a preview. Customer ratings and reviews will help you make an informed choice.

04 Buy and download

To buy a song, tap on the price button on the right. To buy the whole album tap the album's price button, then tap Buy Album. Enter your Apple ID password so that iTunes can take your payment. The desired song or album will then be downloaded to your iPhone.

Create and save Genius playlists on your iPhone

Creating your own special playlists is great but by letting the iPhone do all the hard work you can get some really cool musical mixes

Keeping track of all the music on your iPhone can be a bit of a pain. It's surprising how much music you can fit onto even just the 16GB version. With all that music it makes sense to keep track of it all and to create playlists so you can easily get access to the tunes you want.

Of course, listening to whole albums is fine, but then we all have our favourite tracks and like to hear them more often than others. Creating playlists manually is a great way of doing this, but it's time consuming and if you don't keep them updated they soon get tiresome.

You could just stick your whole music collection on random, but even this throws up issues like those hidden tracks or fillers that ruin a smooth transition, or the odd song you're bored of hearing. There are also those songs that you wonder why you ever downloaded them! The best solution may well be Genius mixes.

Apple has created a tool that lets you select a track and automatically create a playlist of music that complements each other. It's a great way of keeping the music going around a certain theme and in the main it's incredibly reliable.

> **"Apple has created a tool to select a track and automatically create a playlist of music that complements each other"**

iPod   Make Genius mixes on the iPhone

01 Open iPod
Fire up your iPhone and then launch the iPod application. Find a song that would make a good foundation for your playlist; this will be the basis of your list, so make sure you pick something good! You'll also want something with plenty of similar music, so the iPhone has something to choose from.

02 Make a Genius mix
When you have found a track that most suits your current mood, tap on it to start it playing. When you're ready, tap the artwork to make the scrubbing and repeat/shuffle controls appear. That swirly atomic symbol in the middle? That's the Genius icon. Tap on it.

Playlists on the iPhone

Create your own
Genius playlist

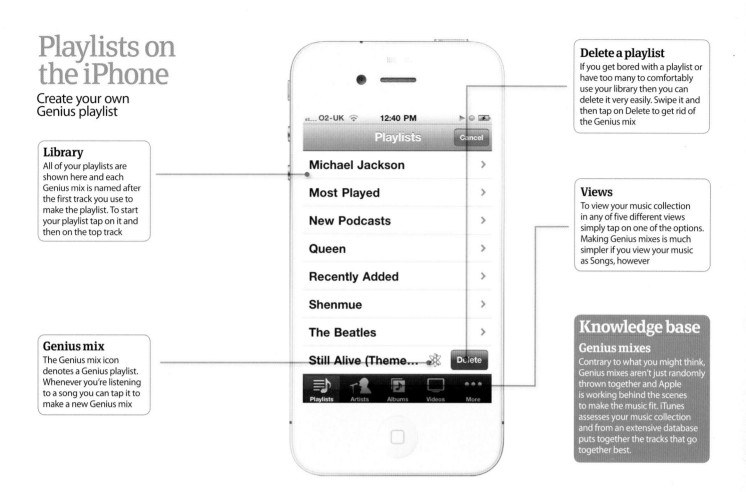

Library
All of your playlists are shown here and each Genius mix is named after the first track you use to make the playlist. To start your playlist tap on it and then on the top track

Genius mix
The Genius mix icon denotes a Genius playlist. Whenever you're listening to a song you can tap it to make a new Genius mix

Delete a playlist
If you get bored with a playlist or have too many to comfortably use your library then you can delete it very easily. Swipe it and then tap on Delete to get rid of the Genius mix

Views
To view your music collection in any of five different views simply tap on one of the options. Making Genius mixes is much simpler if you view your music as Songs, however

Knowledge base

Genius mixes
Contrary to what you might think, Genius mixes aren't just randomly thrown together and Apple is working behind the scenes to make the music fit. iTunes assesses your music collection and from an extensive database puts together the tracks that go together best.

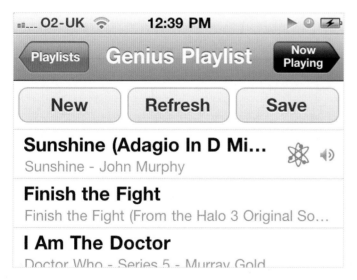

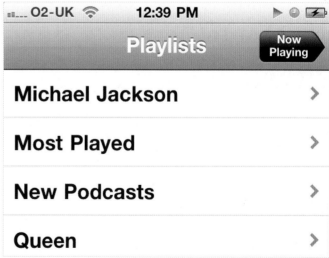

03 Assess your mix
You'll see that a new playlist called Genius has been added to your library and that songs have already been populated to it. If you don't like the tracks simply tap on Refresh, or if you would prefer to choose a different starting point tap New.

04 Save your playlist
Once you are happy with the tracks that are on your playlist all you have to do is tap on Save. The playlist that was called Genius is now renamed to the starting track of your Genius mix. By default a Genius mix contains 25 tracks.

Use iTunes to get movies

Discover recent Hollywood blockbusters by browsing Apple's iTunes Store via your iPhone, then download and enjoy the movies on the move!

The iPhone is the perfect way to enjoy a movie on the move (or tucked up in bed!) thanks to its gorgeous screen. The beauty of the 3G connection means that you can browse a wide selection of new and classic movies via the iPhone's iTunes app, then download them to rent or keep.

Indeed, renting a film via the iPhone couldn't be more convenient or easy, as it saves you the time and effort of driving to the local rental store and can be done anywhere – even in the departure lounge as you're waiting for a long-distance flight. You also don't need to worry about being fined for returning the film late either, as the movie simply becomes unavailable 48 hours after you start watching it, avoiding those annoying extra charges.

If you use your iPhone to buy a movie to boost your digital film collection, you can transfer it to your desktop computer after you have watched it, so it won't permanently hog valuable space on your iPhone. You can always pop the film back on the iPhone at a later date if you fancy watching it on a long train journey, or if it's something you just have to watch again!

"Renting a film via the iPhone couldn't be more convenient, as it saves you the effort of driving to the local rental store and can be done anywhere"

iTunes Downloading a movie

01 Open iTunes on the iPhone

Tap on the iTunes app to launch it. It will take you to the iTunes Store's homepage. Tap on the Videos icon at the bottom of the screen. You'll see thumbnails linking to new and noteworthy movies, as well as colourful banners advertising the latest film releases.

02 Browse a genre

To find the type of film you enjoy, scroll down to the bottom and tap Genres. This lets you fine-tune your browsing to Sci-Fi & Fantasy or Drama, for example. Tap on a genre to access its page. You can then scroll down through the most popular movies.

Get movies from iTunes

Browse by genre then rent or buy a movie to enjoy on your iPhone

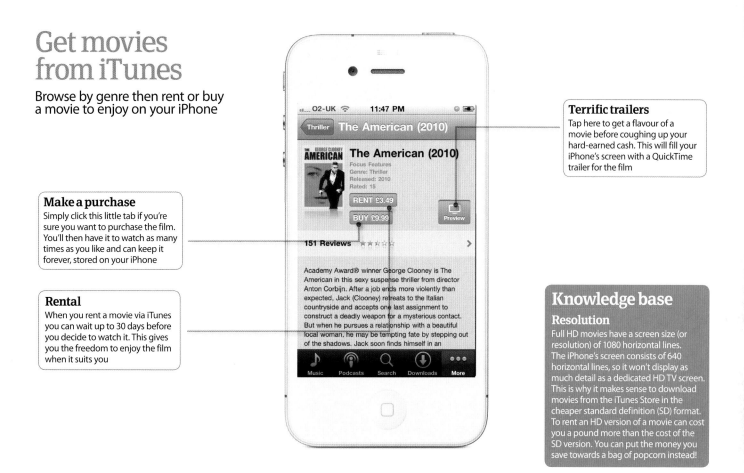

Make a purchase
Simply click this little tab if you're sure you want to purchase the film. You'll then have it to watch as many times as you like and can keep it forever, stored on your iPhone

Rental
When you rent a movie via iTunes you can wait up to 30 days before you decide to watch it. This gives you the freedom to enjoy the film when it suits you

Terrific trailers
Tap here to get a flavour of a movie before coughing up your hard-earned cash. This will fill your iPhone's screen with a QuickTime trailer for the film

Knowledge base
Resolution
Full HD movies have a screen size (or resolution) of 1080 horizontal lines. The iPhone's screen consists of 640 horizontal lines, so it won't display as much detail as a dedicated HD TV screen. This is why it makes sense to download movies from the iTunes Store in the cheaper standard definition (SD) format. To rent an HD version of a movie can cost you a pound more than the cost of the SD version. You can put the money you save towards a bag of popcorn instead!

03 Read reviews

Tap on a thumbnail to discover more about a particular movie. Scroll down to read some iTunes customer reviews, as this will help you decide if the film is worth buying, renting or avoiding. You can even write your own if you have something to say about a movie.

04 Watch a preview

Most movies will let you watch a free preview if you want to see what the film is like. Tap on the big Preview button on the right to watch the trailer. If you're just trying to kill a few minutes, this in itself isn't a bad way to pass the time.

Use the App Store on your iPhone

One of the best things about your iPhone is that it can be upgraded on the go. The App Store allows you to make the iPhone even more magical than it already is…

The iPhone is, as Steve Jobs says, magical, and a major part of the magic is that you can expand its capabilities with cheap or even free apps. The App Store has been a roaring success for Apple, with over 400,000 applications to choose from – not to mention the $1 billion that it's made for developers.

The number and range of applications on offer is quite stunning. The App Store has applications to help you plan large projects, word processors, web browsers; the list is endless. The software tends to be incredibly good value too – it's amazing what your iPhone can do with just a 59p investment. The fact that the App Store is right there on your iPhone means that you can buy stuff on the go, too.

With so much choice it can be quite difficult to discover exactly what you want, but the App Store on the iPhone is easy enough to use when you know how, so follow these simple steps to learn more…

"It's amazing what your iPhone can do with just a 59p investment"

Genius
This feature works for apps as well as music, making recommendations based on your purchases

Updates
The App Store will automatically check for free updates to your apps. Check here regularly to grab them for new features, bug fixes and more

App Store
Learn how to use the App Store on your iPhone

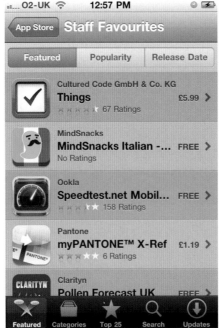

01 Getting started
Once you've set up an account, simply tap the App Store icon to get started. The first screen has some recent notable apps.

02 Staff Favourites
If you'd like to see what the staff at Apple are interested in, tap What's Hot at the top and then hit the Staff Favourites button.

03 App of the Week
Each week a new app is chosen to be the app of the week. These are often surprising and it's a great way to find a really good app.

04 Find apps

If you know the name of the app you want, simply tap the search button and type it there. It searches by both name and description.

05 Charts

Apple lets you see the top paid apps and the top free ones. Simply tap on the Top Charts button at the bottom of the screen to see what they are.

06 What's Hot

The What's Hot section lists some of the best apps that might not have made it to the charts yet. Tap What's Hot at the top of the Store.

07 Categories

If you're not sure what you want but have a general idea, tap the Categories button. This shows 20 different groups of apps.

08 Buying an app

When you're ready to buy an app, getting it is simple. Tap on the price and it will change to 'Buy App'. Tap again and then enter your password.

09 Updating an app

Over time, and more regularly than you might imagine, apps get updated. Tap on Updates and then either Update All or pick apps to update.

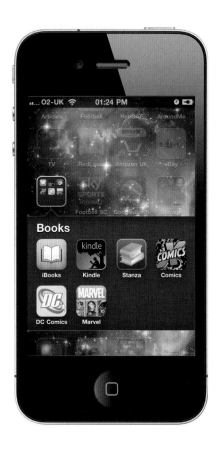

Download iBooks from the App Store

iBooks is your one-stop shop for all the latest releases and free, out-of-copyright titles. Here's how to get it from the App Store

I f you like reading on your iPhone then you really need to get hold of iBooks. It's an app for all the titles you have downloaded and also a book store where you can buy new and popular books from all the leading publishers. There are also free titles like the *iPad User Guide* and out-of-copyright classics like *Treasure Island* and *The Art Of War*.

The interface is split into two sections: one is the bookshelf for all your titles, and the other is the store. To read your books you simply tap on them on the bookshelf. Before you do all that though you need to get the iBooks app onto your iPhone, and this really is a very simple process indeed. If you are away from your computer with iTunes installed and want to get iBooks and download it directly to your iPhone, you're in the right place.

We will guide you through it all with some really simple steps that will get you reading digitally in no time at all.

"iBooks lets you buy new and popular books from all the leading publishers and get free out-of-copyright classics like Treasure Island"

App Store — Download the iBooks app

01 Go to the App Store
The first step is to turn your iPhone on and make sure you are connected to the internet. If you aren't then there's unfortunately no way that this can work, but the iBooks app is small enough to download over 3G, so don't worry if you're not on Wi-Fi. Find the App Store icon and tap on it.

02 Using the Store
With a live internet connection the App Store will appear displaying all the latest titles in a variety of categories. The currently promoted apps appear at the top of the page. To save looking for the iBooks app we simply need to use the Search function.

Installing the application

Discover everything about the latest version of the iBooks app

Latest information
Apps get updated all the time and iBooks is no exception. Scroll down for all the info and screenshots

More information
If you tap on the iBooks icon in the App Store you get a more detailed page of information and the option to download it

Install the app
Tap on the word 'Free' under the icon for the app and it turns into 'Install'. Tap on this to download and install it

Knowledge base

Copyright and books

Copyright law is different from country to country, though the EU has tried to standardise it across the European Union. Many countries have signed up to the Berne Convention, and in those, any author is automatically granted copyright to their work without having to register it. Copyright, however, doesn't last forever and in most cases it ceases either 50 or 70 years after the death of the author. That's why there are classic novels available on iBooks for free. The copyright on them has lapsed and they can be reprinted or republished.

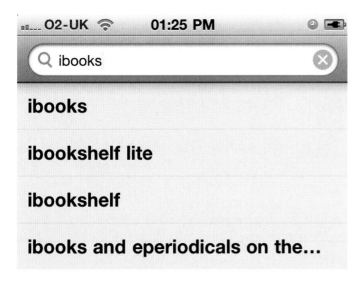

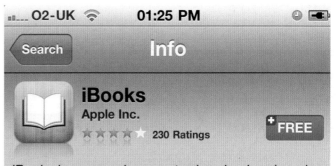

03 Search for iBooks

Tap on the Search button at the bottom of the App Store screen. Type the word 'iBooks' with the keyboard. As soon as you start, the full word may appear in the Suggestions box. Either finish typing or tap on the suggested word. Tap Search on the keyboard.

04 Install the app

The first result should be iBooks. To install it tap on it and then on the word 'Free' next to the icon. This changes to 'Install App'. Tap on that and you will be prompted for your iTunes password. Enter it and iBooks will begin downloading to your Home screen.

Getting started

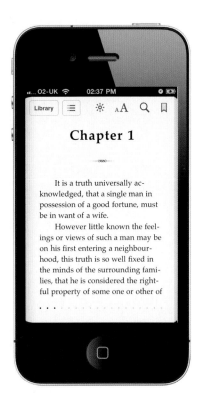

Purchase an eBook

Learn how to open up to a whole world of digital reading

I t's very easy to get lost in a world of crazy apps, accelerometers and multi-touch gestures, but the iPhone is a fantastic eBook reader. It obviously has a number of advantages over the Kindle in that it can do a great deal more than a dedicated device, but on a purely eBook-reading scale, the iPhone is still one of the most advanced out there, especially for its size. What's more is that Apple already has a tried and tested way to deliver eBooks directly to its device: namely the iTunes Store. Apple hasn't just bundled the new books into that system, though, because it's created

a separate space for these so that users can be sure of what they are downloading.

Once you have downloaded the app, iBooks holds all of your eBooks, and from there you can access the custom-built iBooks Store to make purchases, which get downloaded directly. The system is magnificent in its simplicity and, like the App Store, it makes impulse buys a regular occurrence. This tutorial will take you through your first download from iBooks so that you can get a feel for the system. It's then up to you to resist buying a library's worth of content on each visit!

> "The iPhone can do a great deal more than a dedicated device and is still one of the most advanced eBook readers out there, especially for its size"

iBooks Purchase a book

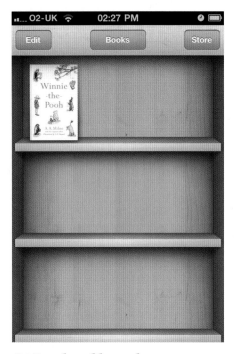

01 Load and launch
You have to download iBooks from the App Store and then, once it's loaded, have a look at the free copy of *Winnie The Pooh*. To purchase your first book, hit the Store button on the top right.

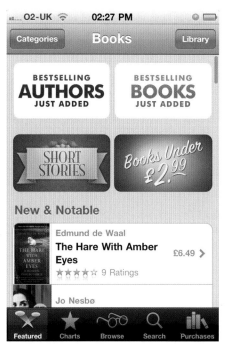

02 Familiar feel
The iBooks Store is very much like the App Store or the iTunes Store. Books are categorised and searchable, and everything is charted so that you can see what is selling best.

03 Charts
There is even a section on the store where you can see the charts so you can pick and download titles from it. You'll find separate lists for free and paid content.

The iBooks Store homepage

Find your way around your new home for digital books

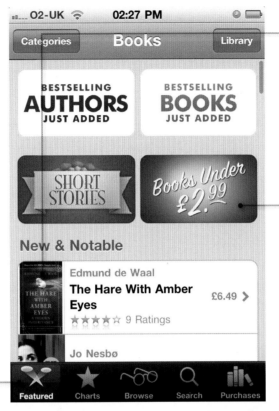

Promo perfection
Again, like the App Store, books are picked by Apple to be featured on the front of the Store. This positioning increases their sales no end, as you can imagine

Easy navigation
Navigating through the Store with your fingers is easy. Tap buttons to see more and tap individual books to get more information

Tabs at the bottom
At the bottom of the interface there are five tabs, which will help you navigate through the Store and also see what you have already bought

Knowledge base

Be prepared
If you know that you are going to be without a data signal for any great period of time it's well worth downloading a couple of books so that you always have some reading material.

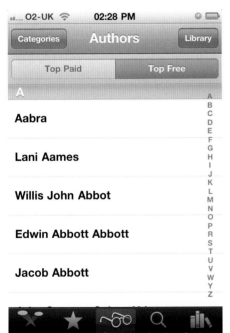

04 Free books

Like the App Store, there are a huge number of free books. These tend to be classics, so you can go ahead and get great content for nothing. There's a ton of free material.

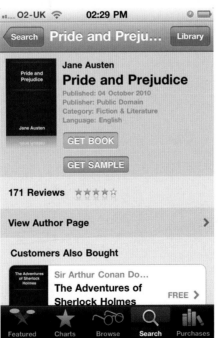

05 Get a book

When you've found a book you want, tap the price followed by 'Get book'. You'll be prompted for your password and, after entering it, the book will download.

06 New books

Your new books will now appear on the bookshelf and you'll see a progress bar as they download. Once downloaded, the book will become available to read at your leisure.

Learn your way around iBooks

Having an eBook reader on the iPhone is very cool, so here's how to customise it to your liking…

When you're reading a book on the iPhone it feels natural, it's easy to do, and we are certain that we'll be doing a lot more reading now that it's so simple to carry books around with us. The beauty of the iPhone interface means that making changes to the way iBooks looks is very, very simple. Users can opt to make text bigger, change the font and alter the brightness of the book without having to leave the page they are reading. Try doing the same three operations on a paper book and you'll see the advantages of reading in a digital format. iBooks is exceptional, so follow our quick tutorial on how to get more from the already excellent reading experience.

> "Try doing these operations on a paper book and you'll see the advantages of reading in a digital format"

True text
Once you have your fonts and the brightness set up how you like, you can read for hours on this device

Scrubber
You can also navigate through the app using the scrubber bar at the bottom of the page. Just drag your finger along the line

iBooks Font, size and brightness

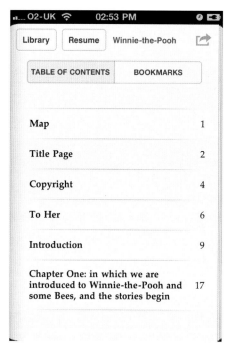

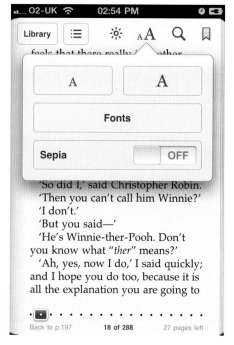

01 Open, bask
Open the iBooks app and then tap on the cover of a book on your shelf that you would like to read. Tap the page to toggle the option buttons.

02 Contents
You can navigate from the contents page to a chapter simply by tapping on it and can return to this screen from the second left icon at the top.

03 Curler
You can flip through pages by dragging from the right-hand side to the left, where you'll see the cool page curl. Or just tap on the right.

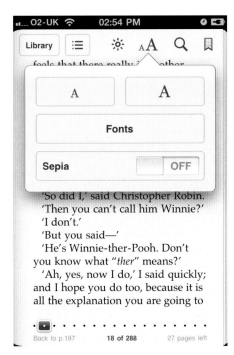

04 Font it

Tap on the 'aA' font button at the top of the page to access the menu where you can alter the book's font and text size.

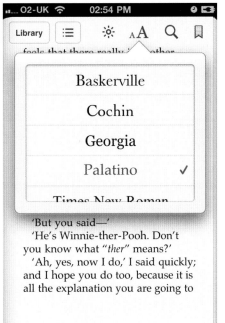

05 Font type

To change the font type, tap the Fonts button and then pick from the available options that are listed in the pop-out window.

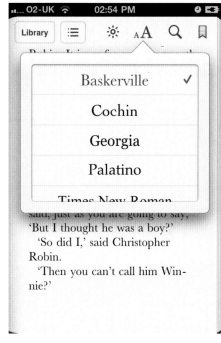

06 Tick it, watch it

Tap the font you wish to select and a tick will appear next to it. As with all the other changes you can make, it happens instantly.

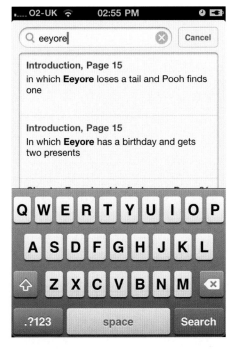

07 Spotlight index

Tap on the magnifying glass to bring up a search field. Every book on the store is fully indexed so you can instantly find individual words in a book.

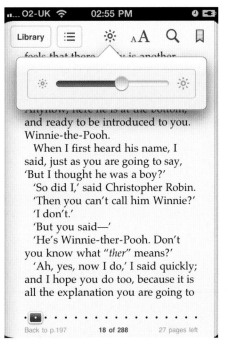

08 Brightness

Tap on the sunshine icon to bring up the brightness settings. This only affects iBooks and doesn't translate to the rest of the iPhone.

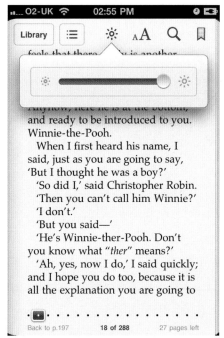

09 Suitable setting

Changing the brightness means that you can alter the reading light to whatever is most comfortable for your eyes.

Creating bookmarks in the iBooks app

Learn how to easily bookmark and highlight your favourite parts in digital books

In the previous tutorials we have introduced you to the digital world of iBooks and all it has to offer you. iBooks is a fantastic eReader that allows you to carry a whole bookcase with you while on the move, customise the fonts, brightness and other settings to suit your needs and create a reading experience like no other.

But having a wealth of books on your iPhone could become hard to find your way around; thankfully, not only are your iBooks organised into a library that's easy to navigate, but you can also bookmark and highlight text so you can easily find the bit you are looking for among the piles and piles on your digital bookshelf.

The ability to highlight text is also a welcome feature. You can even select what colour you want to highlight the text in, which helps when you want to colour code certain bits to signify certain things, or you want to return to them at a later date. This is particularly useful for textbook research. In this step-by-step tutorial we will show you how to easily use bookmarks with iBooks.

"Bookmark and highlight text so you can easily find the bit you are looking for among the piles and piles on your digital bookshelf"

iBooks Using Bookmarks in iBooks

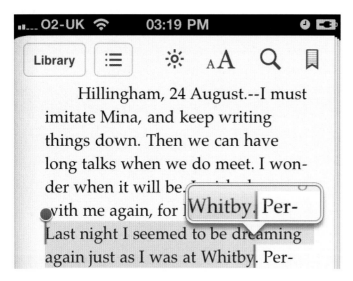

01 Select text to highlight
Double tap anywhere (or press on a word) on the book to open the Options bar. Move the blue circles to select a region of text that you want to bookmark or highlight. It is similar to the cut-copy-paste mechanism available everywhere in iOS.

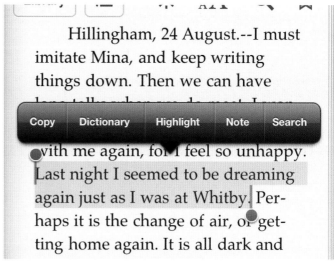

02 Highlight the selected text
Once the text has been selected, tap on the highlight button found in the Options bar. Selecting the list icon next to the Library button will then take you to the bookmark menu, which includes your highlights. Tapping on the bookmark you want will take you to the relevant page.

iBooks interface
Having a look inside iBooks

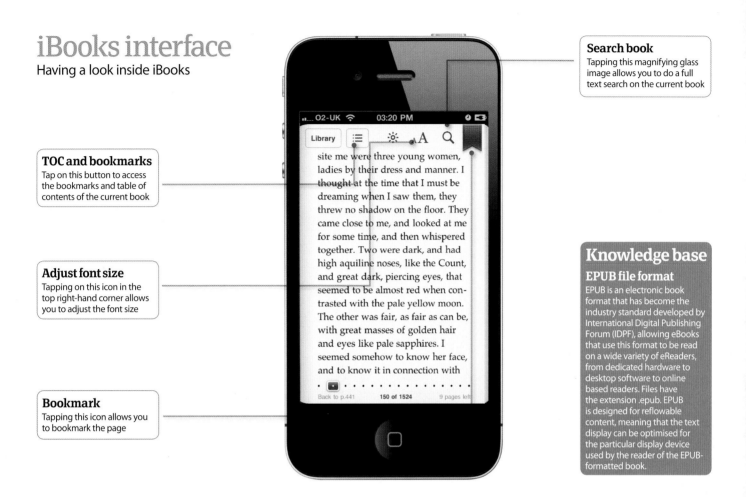

Search book
Tapping this magnifying glass image allows you to do a full text search on the current book

TOC and bookmarks
Tap on this button to access the bookmarks and table of contents of the current book

Adjust font size
Tapping on this icon in the top right-hand corner allows you to adjust the font size

Bookmark
Tapping this icon allows you to bookmark the page

03 Highlight text
The highlight is designed to look like it's been gone over with a highlighter pen. By tapping on it, you can change colour if you want to differentiate your highlights for different purposes, add a note of your own or remove the highlight entirely.

04 Change colour of highlighted text
You can change the colour of bookmarked text to organise it better. You can choose from five colours, namely yellow, green, blue, pink and purple. To change the colour, tap on the highlighted text, tap the Colors… option and then select a different colour.

The next step

Learn your way around the iPhone's more advanced features

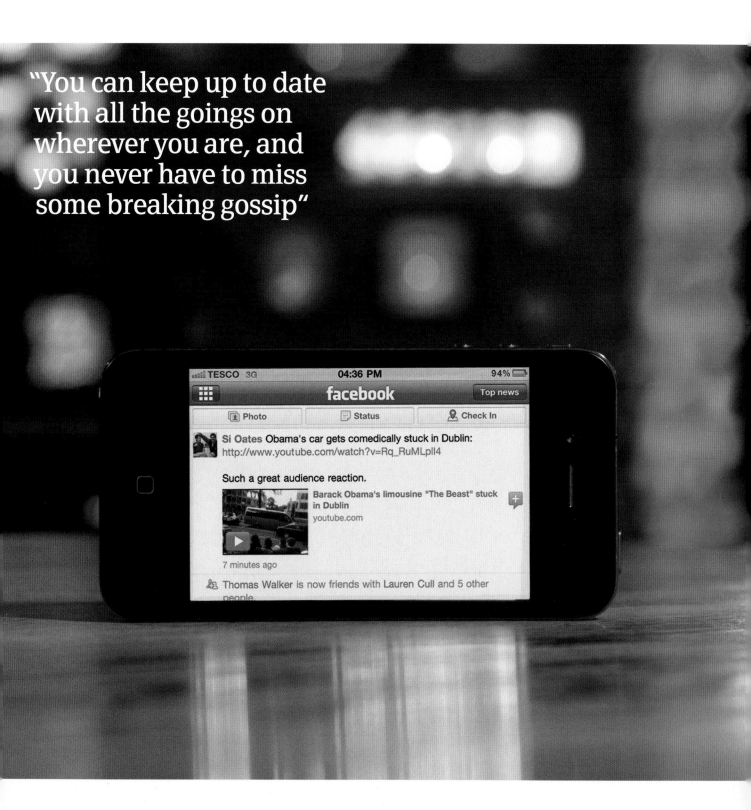

"You can keep up to date with all the goings on wherever you are, and you never have to miss some breaking gossip"

Learn your way around FaceTime

Learn how to make a FaceTime call for free. Calls can be initiated in different ways so it will pay to know the best methods

FaceTime is not a new idea, but with Apple behind it the chances of it becoming widespread are much higher than when 3G was initially launched. Video calling was supposed to herald a new dawn of mobile communication, but high costs and poor coverage got in the way. Apple has chosen to allow video calling only under Wi-Fi, which limits flexibility, but the benefits are that the calls are free and you can be sure of better video quality.

It will feel strange at first because video communication is an unknown experience for most people and you may feel nervous communicating with people this way, but once you are over the stage fright you will find voice communication almost flat in comparison. At some stage the feature may be enabled for everyone to work on 3G and this should make it even more widespread, and with it available on Mac and iPod touch too this is a good time to get used to the technology.

The system is integrated into iOS well and this ensures that you should be up and communicating in just a matter of minutes, but some simple tips will help you get started and even save you some money in the long run.

"You will find voice communication flat in comparison"

FaceTime Understand FaceTime in a few minutes

01 Where is it?

There is no FaceTime icon because it is a feature that is embedded in the Phone app and also Contacts. Go to the Phone app and make a call, and you'll see a FaceTime button in the grid.

02 Make your call visual

Make a call to a friend with an iPhone 4, iPad 2, new iPod touch or camera-equipped Mac. Once the call has started, tap the FaceTime icon to see each other and start talking.

03 Check yourself

During the call you'll see a small window in the top-right corner, which lets you quickly know if you are pointing the camera so that the recipient can see you.

Get the most out of the FaceTime app

A quick guide to finding your way around FaceTime

Look at yourself
The top-right-hand window gives you a view of yourself so that you can make sure you are positioned correctly. It is all too easy to continually check your own appearance, though!

Flipping
Just tap this icon to flip between cameras; the front camera to show your face and the back camera to show where you are

Quality
The quality of the video presentation is very good and it works much better than solutions we have used in the past. Sound and video keep in sync very well

Muting
The mute icon at the bottom is useful if you need to quickly mute the call because you have to talk to someone else

Knowledge base
Are you both ready?
One crucial point to remember about FaceTime is that both parties on a call currently need to be using Wi-Fi to start the call. You may have to go through a quick routine of checking by text message before you start, or at the very least expect a few calls to be rejected due to lack of Wi-Fi on the receiving end.

04 Spin around
Tapping the reverse icon in the bottom right will spin the cameras around so that your recipient can see what the main iPhone camera can see instead of the small forward-mounted camera.

05 Use your contacts
You can also use the Contacts app to initiate a call and save all of your minutes. Go to a contact and tap the FaceTime icon at the bottom. This only works if you have the number of their device.

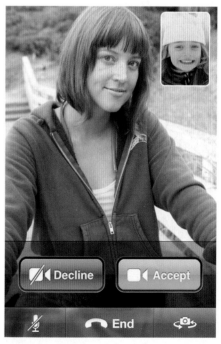

06 Time to talk
When you receive a FaceTime request you will see a visual notification as well as hear an audible alert. Simply accept or reject the video call by tapping the icons.

Take your first picture

Discover how to set up and use your iPhone's excellent camera to take a photograph that you can be proud of

The iPhone's camera capabilities have grown in the last few years and its popularity has spurned a whole new photographic shooting style, iPhonography. With so much creative flexibility on the iPhone it has encouraged more people to start shooting and sharing again, with family albums being composed on mobile phones and uploaded online.

Offering up two cameras, the iPhone 4 has packed in a five megapixel camera on the back with LED flash, for photographic shooting and a VGA camera on the front for optional FaceTime video calling. You can compose and preview your shots on the front screen and make simple adjustments to the camera settings with the tap of a finger. Fantastic for capturing quickly on the go, you are always likely to have your iPhone on hand and with impressive image quality you won't be disappointed with your snapshot results.

Also featuring a 5x digital zoom the camera allows you to shoot up close and can stay in focus from a distance of around ten centimetres, making it great for any macro close-ups. The iPhone camera comes with a GPS style offering as well which, when switched on, can tag photographs and video with location data, including your geographical co-ordinates using GPS, Wi-Fi or cell tower co-ordinates, letting you know exactly where your photograph or video was taken.

With the iPhone camera's popularity on the increase there are now a range of photography-related apps available to download from the App Store. iPhonographers now benefit from being able to shoot using filtered effects or make image-editing alterations at the tap of a finger, all conveniently on their iPhone.

Set up and start shooting and sharing by following our simple how-to steps below.

Photos Take a photograph on your iPhone

01 Set up stills shooting

Begin by selecting the Camera icon, this will activate the camera and set the screen to view mode. Ensure your camera is set to stills shooting with the switch set to camera not video.

02 Compose and focus

Compose your shot on the screen and tap where in the frame you want the camera to focus. Aim to keep the foreground sharp by selecting the areas that are closer to the camera.

03 Zooming in

You can use the camera's 5x digital zoom to get in closer to your subject. Select the zoom slider on the screen and drag the cursor from left to right to zoom in or out until you're happy.

Taking a photograph

A look at how to set up your camera

Front or back
The camera swivel icon allows you to switch between using the camera on the back and the camera on front of the iPhone

Stills or motion?
Tap the slider to switch between stills camera shooting or hi-def video capture

Use the flash
Select the flash icon to opt between the automatic, on or off set-up depending on the lighting conditions of your shot

View the image
Tap the image thumbnail to preview your last capture in the camera roll album

Knowledge base

Enhance colour
The iPhone 4's HDR (High Dynamic Range) feature allows the camera to take three different exposures of the same scene and compress them together, essentially creating one image that appears more true to life in colour and contrast. You can choose to save both your HDR capture and normal capture by going to Settings>Photo and selecting keep normal photo so that both images are saved. Check out the tutorial on the next page for a more detailed look at HDR.

04 Set up flash
The in-built LED light works like a standard camera flash. Fantastic for use in low light, select the flash icon and choose between automatic, on or off. Set the camera to Auto for best results.

05 HDR setting
The iPhone's HDR setting can also be selected on the screen and works best in daylight while holding the camera steady, giving you much sharper results.

06 Capturing and previewing
Once you're happy, press the shutter button in the centre of the toolbar. The shot will be saved to your Camera Roll and can be viewed by tapping the image at the bottom of the screen.

HDR photography on your iPhone

Capture better shots by using the native HDR on your iPhone

For those that aren't already familiar with the concept, HDR imaging (also known as high dynamic range imaging) is a set of techniques used in photography to produce images that contain a greater range of light intensity and tonal variation. By taking the same shot using different exposures (usually a minimum of three) and overlaying them, you can create an almost three-dimensional effect.

This effect can be created manually on a DSLR by taking three shots at different exposures – one set at auto, then one underexposed and one overexposed – and layering them together in Adobe Photoshop (or another image editor). However, it's becoming more common to find cameras that have an automatic HDR feature which will do all the hard work for you. The iPhone 4 now has the facility to achieve this effect automatically, combining multiple exposures into a single HDR image to give you better shots without the hard work.

Generally it's always better to try HDR with an object that isn't moving, as the multiple exposure can create blur. Landscapes are a good subject to try, or something that has good contrast and tonal variety. And it's essential to try to keep your hand as still as possible.

"The iPhone has the ability to give you better shots without the hard work"

Camera   Use native HDR on your iPhone

01 Open camera

Head up to the camera icon at the top-right corner of your Home screen by default and give it a tap to open – just as if you were taking a picture normally.

02 Wait

You may have to wait a few seconds for the camera to load. You can see a live view in the small box at the bottom left of the interface or a thumbnail of your most recent photo.

03 Switch HDR on

When the camera loads up, you'll see that in the top centre of the viewfinder there's a button that says 'HDR Off'. Tap this to switch HDR on. Repeat to turn it off again if you want.

Take better shots with HDR

Use native HDR, or an app, for photos with more tonal variety

HDR icon
When viewing your photos, HDR images are indicated by a small icon at the top-left corner of the interface

Keep still
The most important thing to remember when using HDR is to choose still objects, preferably landscapes, and also to keep your hand as steady as possible

Rear only
The iPhone 4 can, unfortunately, employ the high dynamic range technique with the rear-facing camera only, not the front one

Tonal variety
You'll notice that by taking photographs using the HDR tool, your images will have improved tonal variety. This image has a bluer sky and better contrast than the non-HDR equivalent

Knowledge base

Pro HDR

If you're keen to experiment further with the HDR technique, there are a plethora of different apps now available on the iTunes Store, offering HDR effects for the iPhone 4. We've tried Pro HDR, which is a snip at £1.19. It generally produces a slightly more extreme effect than the native HDR.

04 Action
You are ready to take your first HDR image. Just hit the shutter icon as normal. Remember to keep your hand as steady as possible because your phone will be taking three photos instead of one.

05 Saving HDR
HDR images take longer to process than normal because there's some number-crunching to be done, so wait a few seconds. The image will be saved to your photo album as usual.

06 View
When the image has been saved, you can view it as normal by tapping on the window in the bottom corner, or by looking it up in your photo album.

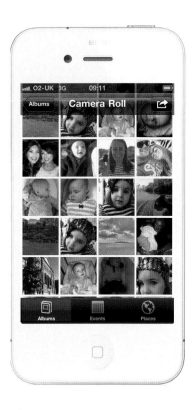

Get to grips with the Photos app

Make use of the sharper, clearer Retina display on the iPhone 4 and view your snaps in the Photos app

The high-resolution Retina display on the iPhone 4 means that your photos will now look better than ever. And what better way is there to view your shots than using the iPhone 4 Photos app?

The crystal-clear Retina display basically offers a higher pixel density, meaning that your eye won't be able to distinguish between individual pixels. This results in much sharper, clearer images. Not only does the Photos app automatically save images that you take with the iPhone camera, but it will also store images from third-party apps such as

Hipstamatic and Pro HDR, enabling you to easily scroll through all of your photographs at the same time. You can also add photos to your iPhone Photos app from iPhoto, by syncing either events or albums in iTunes – the perfect way to create a portable album.

This tutorial will show you how to master some of the new features in the revamped Photos app, including viewing, sorting, organising and sharing your images, along with viewing Places information about them. This will give you easy access to your images wherever you are.

"The Retina display on the iPhone 4 means that your photos will look better than ever"

Photos app View your snaps in the Photos app

01 Open
The Photos app is the blue icon with the sunflower. It's usually located on the top right of the interface, between Camera and Calendar.

02 Albums
The first page is 'Albums'. 'Camera Roll' refers to the photos you have taken. If you sync albums or events they appear in the folders underneath.

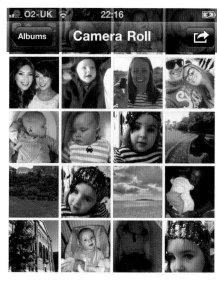

03 Open Album
Tap 'Camera Roll' to view photos taken on your iPhone. The bottom of the interface will indicate how many photos and videos are in the album.

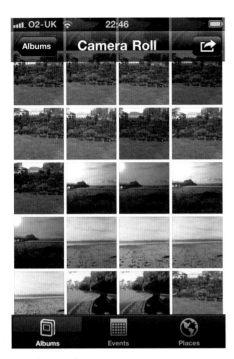

04 Organise

Tapping the arrow at the top right will give you the option to organise your files without opening them. This is ideal if you want to delete images.

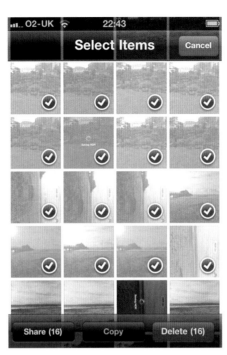

05 Share, Copy, Delete

Select the images to be organised and a tick will appear. Tap the red button to delete, 'Copy' to copy and 'Share' to send it via email or MMS.

06 Viewing

When you've finished, you'll return to the Camera Roll. To view an image just tap on it. To return to the Camera Roll, tap the button in the top left.

07 Information

The information will disappear after a second or so – tap once to get it back up again. Tap the bin icon to delete the image or the arrow to share it.

08 Swipe

Swipe across the screen to move between images. To zoom, hold two fingers on the screen and slide them outwards. To zoom out, reverse the motion.

09 Places

The iPhone saves the location info for images. Tap 'Places', then the red pin to see how many images were taken there. Tap the arrow to view them.

Print from the Photos app

The iPhone's camera is a great way to take photos. Now learn how to print them out, over the air…

The iPhone 4 has one of the best cameras available on any smartphone, and the pictures it takes really are fantastically high-quality. Not only that, but there are a number of apps out there that allow you to add effects and styles to your photos, meaning that you can create a masterpiece while you're on the move with very little effort.

Recently, social networks have become the primary way to share your photos with friends, posting them to your Facebook page, or putting them on your Flickr account. While it's great to be able to take photos and share them digitally, sometimes it's nicer to have a hard copy of some of your best shots to show your family, or even hang on your wall. With the release of the iPhone 4, Apple announced a new feature that it called

AirPrint, which allows iOS devices to print wirelessly on certain printers that are connected to the same Wi-Fi network. Currently there are only 17 printers that work with Apple's AirPrint technology, all of which are built by HP, but if you are lucky enough to own one of these printers (or if Apple increases the number of compatible devices in the future) you will be able to print without connecting any wires to your iPhone.

If you have an older iPhone, you'll need to make sure you're running the latest version of iOS to ensure you have the ability to use AirPrint, but once you're connected, it's really simple to connect to your printer. Within a few minutes you'll have the photograph from your iPhone printed out and in your hands. Now let's have a look at the steps involved in making this happen.

Photos Print your photos wirelessly

01 Take a shot
The first step in this process is obviously to take a great photograph! Get snapping with your phone, and take a photo you want to print out and show to everyone you know.

02 Find your photo
When you've taken your photo it will be moved to the Camera Roll folder, in the Photos app. You can also access this folder through the Camera app by touching the bottom corner of the screen.

03 Select multiple photos
If you want to print more than one photo, that's also possible. Touch the button in the top right of the screen, then tap the photos you want to select. From this menu, you need to touch Print.

Choosing your prints

The best ways to choose which photos you want to print

Normal view
The standard view will show the photos in a normal view, as small squares that you can scroll through. It's the best way to select multiple photos quickly

Faces
The Faces tab will only apply if you have synced your photos with iPhoto on Mac. It will group photos by people who are in them, making it easier to choose photos of certain friends

Places
Finally, the Places menu will show you where your photos were taken. You can zoom in or out to view more closely. This is all done using the iPhones GPRS features

Events
The Events tab will show your photos ordered into events. If you have have photos from your computer uploaded onto your phone they'll be sorted into albums here

Knowledge base

Available printers
If you want to find out the full list of AirPrint-enabled printers, visit Apple's website at **www.apple. com**, and search for AirPrint. You can also buy one of the models that works with your iPhone from the Apple Online Store.

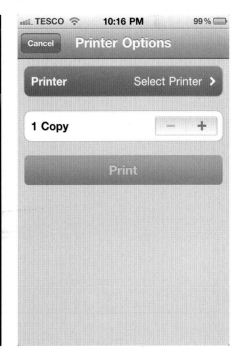

04 Move and resize

When you open the photo you want you can still scroll through the rest of the album as normal, but zoom in and pan around as much as you like to make sure your shot looks as good as it can.

05 Print

When you've found the photo you want and scaled to a level that works well, touch the Menu icon in the bottom left-hand corner of the screen. This menu will appear, so touch print.

06 Select Printer

When you touch Print, this menu will appear. You can search for your printer using the top option. You can also change the number of copies to print. When you're ready, touch Print.

Record HD video

The iPhone 4 has brought with it HD video recording and Apple has cleverly made the process much easier than on most smartphones

Recording video on a mobile should be easy, but it rarely is in the smartphone world. However, Apple has made the process as simple as can be and in this tutorial we are going to show you how to take a video, view it on your phone and share it with others, without even touching a desktop computer.

The quality of the iPhone 4 camera makes capturing special moments in all their glory as realistic as you could wish for and there is a lot happening behind the scenes to help you with focusing, sound capture and the other techniques that you often have to deal with when taking videos. There are, however, some ways in which you can still have control over the videos you are taking, and understanding these will be crucial to capturing the best quality possible, but there's nothing here to scare you off.

The large screen on the iPhone 4 means that you are able to view exactly what you are recording accurately and this will help, but some practice is a good first step so that you can tap the on-screen icons without shaking the phone too much. There are no physical buttons on the iPhone to control video capture and this can feel slightly cumbersome at first, but over time you will see the benefits as your results improve. These quick steps will get you off to a flying start.

"The quality of the iPhone camera makes capturing special moments in all their glory as realistic as you could wish for"

HD video recording Capture moments in HD

01 Getting started

Start by opening the Camera app. Once you have done so there isn't a lot going on, but you will soon feel at home with the icons you need to use, especially if you've already taken stills.

02 Go to video

At the bottom right you will see an icon with a slider. Simply slide it to the right, or just tap it, and you will enter video mode. Tapping it again will, of course, take you back.

03 Get the lighting right

In the top left is the Flash icon. If you tap this you're given three options: Auto, On and Off. It's best to select auto so that the lighting is set for you, based on ambient light conditions.

Making the most of your home movies

Get to grips with the iPhone 4's video camera and all its features

Lighting
Tapping the top-left icon offers you the Flash options; Auto, On and Off. Setting Auto will make it quicker to take videos in the future

Focusing
You can focus a part of the screen at any time by simply tapping once. It is good practice to do this on your subject before you start recording

Timing
The timer will run while you are recording a clip and sits unobtrusively in the corner. This is useful if you have a set time limit for your recordings

Switching
Tapping the bottom-right icon switches you between stills capture and video recording. It will remain in the state you last left it when exiting the app

Knowledge base
Sharing your work
Once you have taken a clip you can share it easily in a variety of ways. Go to the Photo application and tap the bottom-left icon where you are presented with options for sending it via email or MMS. You can also send it to MobileMe or publish it directly onto YouTube without ever touching a desktop computer.

04 Your first recording
Now just tap the record button and away you go. A timer will pop up showing how long you have been recording for. Bear in mind that HD video is quite large – about 100MB per minute.

05 Focus
Before or during your recording tap the screen to focus on a particular area of the screen. This works very well and will become second nature after a few recordings.

06 Record yourself
Tapping the top-right icon will switch cameras and you can then make a recording of yourself speaking into the phone. This is the camera FaceTime uses.

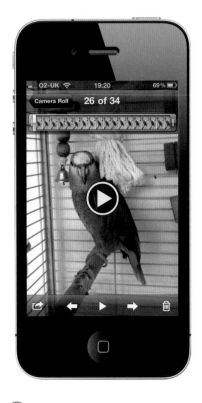

Shoot and share your videos

A notable feature of the iPhone is built-in support for sharing videos. Here we show you how to shoot a video and then share it…

Your iPhone travels everywhere with you and this means that you're always ready to capture that special moment on video. If you own an iPhone 3GS, a tap of the camera toggle switches from photo to video. You're then ready to record in portrait or widescreen landscape.

If you own an iPhone 4, you can record clips in high definition and as a bonus, the backside illumination sensor delivers great-looking video in all settings. Shooting video is straightforward – just tap or slide the switch to the Video icon and then tap

the Record button. To stop recording, just tap the button again.

And when you capture a special moment, what better way to show off your talent than to share the clip with others? Your iPhone sports a number of video-sharing features and an MMS message is just one option. You can also select a video from the Camera Roll, attach it to a new email message and it is ready to send. For the more adventurous, publishing to your MobileMe gallery or YouTube is just a tap away.

> "For the more adventurous, publishing to your MobileMe gallery or YouTube is just a tap away"

Camera Shoot and share a video

01 Shoot the video
The first step is to shoot a video clip. Tap or slide the switch to the Video icon and press the record button to start shooting. Press it again when you have finished.

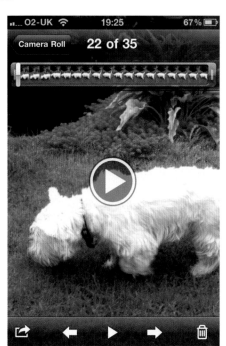

02 Locate clip
Get the feel of shooting video clips and then tap Photos and then Camera Roll, and browse until you locate one you like. Tap the Play button to play the clip or scrub through along the top.

03 Email Video
To email the video tap the share icon in the bottom left and select Email Video. The clip is now compressed. Choose the recipients, type a subject and then click Send.

Shoot and share a video easily

Send your movie masterpieces to friends and family

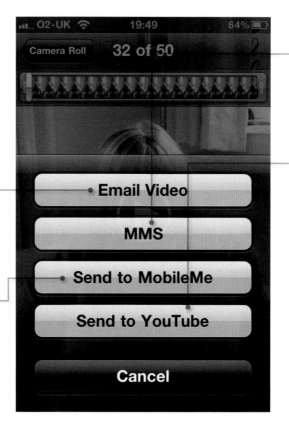

Share by email
You can also share a video clip with others via email. Find a video that you wish to share, tap the Send icon, select Email Video, enter the recipients' names and hit Send

MobileMe Gallery
If you have a MobileMe account, your iPhone will let you upload and publish videos directly to your MobileMe Gallery. This is a great way to share those special moments

MMS
If you want to share a video via MMS, shoot a clip, open the Camera Roll, locate the video, tap the Send icon and then MMS. Enter the recipient's number and tap Send

Upload to YouTube
Your iPhone lets you publish videos to YouTube. Tap the Play icon and then Send to YouTube. Sign in to your account, enter the publishing information and hit Publish

Knowledge base

Share via MMS
If you are in the middle of a text message conversation and see something that you would like to video, tap the Camera icon in Messages and you can record a clip and send it to the person via MMS. Select Take Photo or Video and when the Camera app opens, move the slider to Video. Shoot your clip and when you have finished, click Use and then Send.

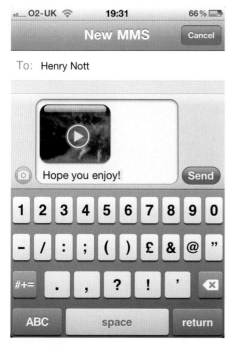

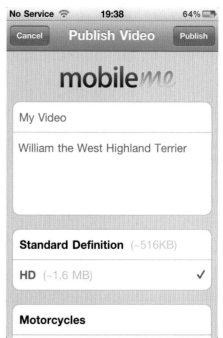

04 MMS
Tap the MMS option to send the video as a multimedia message. Just enter a recipient's number, type some text and hit the Send button. Bear in mind that you may be charged for this.

05 Send to YouTube
You can put your video on YouTube. Tap Send to YouTube, sign in to your account, type a description, select the definition and category, and tap Publish.

06 Send to MobileMe
If you have a MobileMe account, tap Send to MobileMe and then Publish to share your video via your Gallery. Your video will be uploaded in a flash.

Getting started with iMovie

Edit your masterpiece without so much as touching a desktop computer

One of the many great things about Apple software is when we get the opportunity to tell people that it will change the way they go about the process of doing things that had previously been long-winded, difficult to do or had been frustrating. Editing movies could easily be labelled any of the above (even on a Mac) but Apple has, with the power of the iPhone 4, given people the opportunity to negate the need to import and edit on a full-sized computer, and instead given you simple tools to do it right on the device you'll use to capture the footage on in the first place. iMovie for iPhone is not an exhaustive editing suite, and as a result it uses a cleverly worked balance, offering simplicity during use and complexity under the hood when necessary. This tutorial will take you through starting your very first movie.

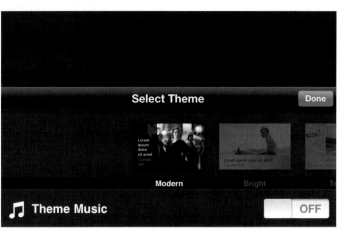

> "The power of the iPhone 4 negates the need to import and edit on a full-sized computer"

Get to know the iMovie for iPhone app

Learn your way around the iMovie app's layout and controls

Great quality
You can instantly see during your edit that the footage you have captured is incredibly detailed and easy to see on the new Retina display. This makes edits easy to accomplish

Edit window
This is the main window for editing your project. Along the bottom you can see the timeline, and in the main window you can see the point at which the playhead sits

Add footage
Tap this button to be taken to your camera where you can shoot a movie directly into the timeline

Knowledge base
The playhead
The playhead is the red line that runs vertically through the timeline. It indicates the place in the timeline that is being shown in the main window. The playhead can be manipulated to help you find places to trim clips and watch them again as you perfect your edit.

Cog
The cog lets you access the settings for the start of the movie

Frames
Along the bottom of the edit window you can see the frames of your movie, and you can drag the playhead through them as and when you decide to trim each clip

iMovie Create your first movie

01 Open and tap

Open up iMovie. You can do this in landscape and portrait, but we recommend that you use landscape as it offers an easier experience.

02 Themes

You can now pick from one of five Apple themes. These have been specially crafted to offer a cool template that will stitch the project together.

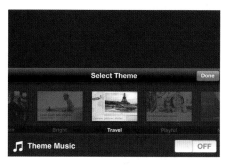

03 Scroll and tap

Use your finger to scroll through the different themes on offer and then tap on the one you'd like to use in your project. Now tap Done.

04 Insert

Follow the prompt and either navigate to your Camera Roll or hit the other button to record a video directly into the timeline.

05 Scroll and pick

If you opt to go to your Camera Roll you will see all of your videos by default. Tapping one will send it into the editing window.

06 Stills and tunes

Along the bottom of the Camera Roll interface there are three tabs, which will allow you to add pre-recorded video or any photos and music.

07 Audio pane

In the Audio pane you have the option to navigate through the sections on your iPod; browse songs by artist, playlist, album or song.

08 iMovie theme music

Apple has a knack of finding great music that you can freely add to your clips. Tap on a song to send it to the edit window.

09 Green bar

Once a music track has been added you can see it as a green bar under your footage. There is no option to edit audio in iMovie mobile.

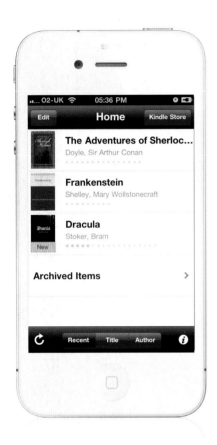

Download and read eBooks using Kindle

Build up a library of books on your iPhone's Kindle app, so you can read your favourite authors on the go

Before eReaders were invented, we had to lug our holiday reading around on slabs of processed dead tree. Printed books, especially chunky hardbacks, took up valuable space in our suitcase, and ate into our precious baggage weight allowance to boot, and no matter how much you love the feel of a solid product in your hands, they were often very inconvenient.

In these digital days, the Kindle app provides a much more convenient way of storing our holiday or day-to-day reading. As well as enabling us to read electronic books (or eBooks) on the iPhone's screen, we can use Kindle to shop for them as well. This saves us the hassle of popping out to the high street bookshop or having to anxiously wait for the postman to deliver books in time for our holiday's departure date. Instead this can all be done in just a few clicks, plus there are a wealth of free books available to download, including some of the all-time classics.

Kindle was initially a handheld tablet from retail giant Amazon to enable book lovers to read digital copies of books. However, iPhone owners can download the free Kindle app and turn their iPhone into a Kindle reader with ease, saving them the expense of buying a dedicated digital book reader.

> "iPhone owners can download the free Kindle app and turn their iPhone into a Kindle reader with ease"

Kindle Learn how to get eBooks onto your iPhone

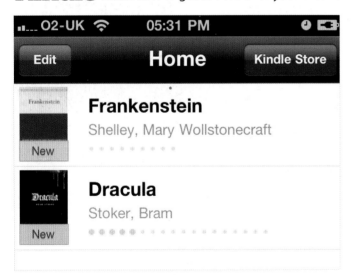

01 Open Kindle

Download the Kindle app from the App Store and install it on your iPhone. Tapping on the Kindle icon takes you to the Home screen. This is where your books will be stored. To find some reading material, click on the 'Kindle Store' button at the top right.

02 Go shopping

The Kindle eBook store is part of the Amazon website, so there are plenty of books to choose from. Peruse one of the featured new books on the Kindle Store's homepage, or browse through your favourite categories by clicking on a link. Like iBooks, Amazon offers some free popular classics.

Interact with a Kindle eBook

Discover the extra bells and whistles you get from an eBook

Dictionary
Not sure of what a word means? Hold down on it to highlight it and a dictionary definition will appear at the top of the screen

Notes and highlight
To help you find a particular bit of text at a later date, hold your finger down on it and drag to make a selection. You can then type in a note or select a highlight colour

Explore further
The Wikipedia link will take you to the related Wikipedia page, giving you a history of the selected letter. The Google link takes you to Google search results

Bo·he·mi·an /bō'hēmēən/ *n.* **1** a native *i* or inhabitant of Bohemia.
2 (also bohemian) a person who has informal and unconventional social

Google   Wikipedia   **Full Definition**

such as his. And yet there was but one woman to him, and that woman was the late Irene Adler, of dubious and questionable memory.

I had seen little of Holmes lately. My marriage had drifted us away from each other. My own complete happiness, and the home-centred interests which rise up around the man who first finds himself master **Note**   **Highlight** nent, were sufficient to absorb all my attention, while Holmes, who loathed every form of society with his whole Bohemian soul, remained in our lodgings in Baker Street, buried among

Knowledge base
Fabulous freebies
As well as downloading sample chapters from many new eBooks, you can download entire books for free using the Kindle eBook reader. This is a great way to catch up with the classics of literature. Simply tap on the link to the online Kindle store to launch it in Safari, then scroll down to the Free Popular Classics section. You can then browse through thousands of books and enjoy adventure tales featuring Conan Doyle's *Sherlock Holmes*, or chill your spine with the work of HP Lovecraft.

(Additional editing by Jose Menendez)

THE ADVENTURES OF SHERLOCK HOLMES

BY

SIR ARTHUR CONAN DOYLE

03 Download your book
Tap on a thumbnail to discover more about a particular book, and read customer reviews to help you make an informed choice. If you fancy buying the book tap the 'Buy now with 1-click' button. Alternatively, download a free sample chapter. Make sure you set it to deliver to your iPhone.

04 Start reading
To read a downloaded book, tap on its cover in your Kindle Home screen. Turn pages by tapping the screen or swiping left or right. You can bookmark a page by tapping the middle of the screen and then tapping the '+' button at the bottom.

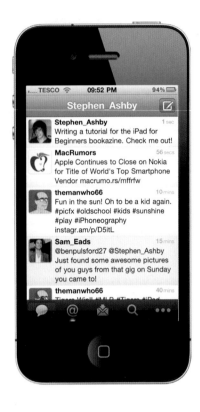

Get started with Twitter

Twitter can be a little daunting to new users, so learn
how to get started and begin tweeting like a pro

Twitter has been a phenomenon since its
launch a few years ago, and is now up
there with the other social networking
giants like Facebook as one of the best ways to
communicate. However, to a newcomer it can be
daunting trying to get started with the network as a
whole, never mind the app for the iPhone.

Twitter allows you to 'follow' other users, who can
be anyone from a friend to a celebrity, and once
you're following them you will see all the 'tweets'
that they send. If they follow you back, they will see
your tweets, so the more interesting your messages,
the more followers you will gather.

Your messages will be completely public and
viewable by anyone (even people who don't have
Twitter accounts), which is something to be aware

of when tweeting, but don't be put off. It's a great
way to keep up with friends, and it also gives you
a chance to see a little more of your favourite
celebrities, and offers you a unique way to contact
them directly by simply putting an @ before their
username in your message. They will then see your
tweet, and may even reply.

So now you know the basic principles of how
Twitter works, it's time to try it out on the iPhone.
It's worth giving it a go on your computer too, but
the iPhone app offers you all the features you would
get at your desk in a much more compact package.
There are several apps available that offer Twitter
access in different ways, so when you're more
confident it might be worth trying some others out
to see which suits you best.

"Twitter allows you to 'follow' other users, anyone from a friend to a celebrity"

Twitter Make a start with Twitter

01 Download the app

Go to the App Store and use the search tool
to search for 'Twitter'. There will be plenty of
options, but you want the official Twitter app, at
the top of this list. Download it for free.

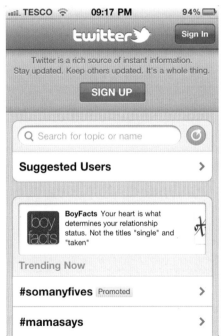

02 Sign up

If you already have a Twitter account you can sign
in from the top-right corner; otherwise, press the
Sign Up button. This screen will also show a few
things that other Twitter users are talking about.

03 Create an account

Twitter won't ask for too many details to create
your account. Input you name and email, then
try to come up with a username, along with a
password. If you need help, press the 'i' button.

The Twitter interface

Getting the lowdown on Twitter

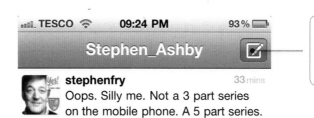

New tweets
Touching this will open up the 'New Tweet' pane shown in Step 6. If you have something on your mind, this is where to go to share it

Direct messages
This is where you can read Direct Messages, or DMs. If you want to say something private to someone, a DM is the best way

Timeline
This is your 'timeline', showing the tweets of everyone that you have decided to follow. You can touch any one you like to see the user and their tweets in more detail

Be notified
If someone mentions you in their tweet you will be notified with a little light under the @ icon. You can mention others by putting @ before their username

⊷ TESCO   09:24 PM   93%

Stephen_Ashby

stephenfry   33 mins
Oops. Silly me. Not a 3 part series on the mobile phone. A 5 part series. It'll be on Radio 4 some time later in the year.

themanwho66   59 mins
Cinco de Mayonnaise #Cincodemayo #May5 #food #toast #mayonnaise #project365 instagr.am/p/D5ayw

Sam_Eads   1 hour
Voted! Feel the power.

Deacyliam   1 hour
@empiremagazine @CTAH1976 @Jack_Marshall_ Pl RT,follow 2 help us get #jackmarshallrules trending,helping 2 raise brain tumour awareness

Knowledge base

Adding photos is simple
When you create a new tweet simply touch the camera icon and you will be given a choice between taking a new photo or using one from your library. Select the photo you like and it will be added automatically to your tweet.

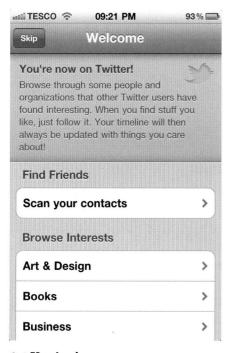

04 You're in
In a few seconds your account will be created. You can then scan the contacts list on your iPhone for your friends' accounts. You can also look for interesting people to follow.

05 Search
If you're looking for a particular Twitter user, you can use the search function. You'll see their profile, showing a brief biography, as well any other details they have added to their accounts.

06 Tweet!
When you've become used to the interface, you can write your first tweet! Touch the icon in the top-right of the screen to bring up this area, then write your message. When finished, press send.

Using the Facebook app on your iPhone

If you have a Facebook account, there's an app that makes it a breeze to use on your iPhone. Here's how to use it

You can, of course, access Facebook through Safari on your iPhone, but it's restricted to the functions of a webpage and is all a bit clunky, with limited support for location services, uploading and chat. But why bother putting yourself through all that hassle when you could simply download the purpose-built iPhone Facebook app?

The app is far better organised and easier to use than the actual website and also uses push notifications to let you know immediately about responses to your actions, posts on your wall or requests from friends as and when they happen.

This means you can keep up to date with all the goings on wherever you are, and you never have to worry about missing out on some breaking gossip!

Once the Facebook app is downloaded and installed on your iPhone, you simply need to enter your email address and Facebook password to get going. You will then have access to all the features you would expect to be able to use on the desktop equivalent of Facebook.

So now let's take a look at some of the functions that make accessing your account on the move as much fun as the main site… you'll never have to be away from your news feed again!

> **"You can keep up to date with all the goings on wherever you are, and you never have to miss some breaking gossip!"**

Facebook Get friendly with this iPhone app

01 Getting started

When the Facebook app is first run you will need to enter your email address and Facebook password to access your account. The app will take you straight to your news feed. You can tap the grid icon in the top left to access the other sections.

02 Live news feeds

On the initial news feed page, there are several options. If you tap on Most Recent you can select from a range of notifications that you want displaying on this page instead. These include ones from pages, status updates, photos, links, video, notes and groups. The page is updated as you scroll.

Quick access to your profile

Here's all the features that revolve around your personal profile

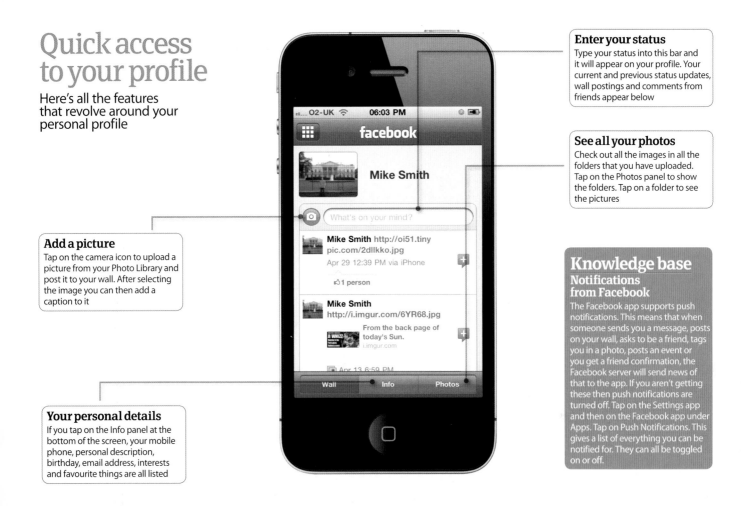

Enter your status
Type your status into this bar and it will appear on your profile. Your current and previous status updates, wall postings and comments from friends appear below

See all your photos
Check out all the images in all the folders that you have uploaded. Tap on the Photos panel to show the folders. Tap on a folder to see the pictures

Add a picture
Tap on the camera icon to upload a picture from your Photo Library and post it to your wall. After selecting the image you can then add a caption to it

Your personal details
If you tap on the Info panel at the bottom of the screen, your mobile phone, personal description, birthday, email address, interests and favourite things are all listed

Knowledge base
Notifications from Facebook
The Facebook app supports push notifications. This means that when someone sends you a message, posts on your wall, asks to be a friend, tags you in a photo, posts an event or you get a friend confirmation, the Facebook server will send news of that to the app. If you aren't getting these then push notifications are turned off. Tap on the Settings app and then on the Facebook app under Apps. Tap on Push Notifications. This gives a list of everything you can be notified for. They can all be toggled on or off.

03 Post your status
The three options on the bar below the Facebook heading allow photos to be uploaded, your status to be posted and to check in using location services to show where you are. Tap on Status and enter what you are doing. Tap on Share when finished.

04 The main hub
Tap on the block of squares in the top left. This is the central hub of the Facebook app allowing access to all the website features including your profile, friends list, news feed, messages, places, groups, events, chat and notes. Tap Photos to see all the folders of images you have uploaded.

100 Essential Apps

Sort the wheat from the chaff with this comprehensive guide to the must-own apps for your iPhone

The writer Theodore Sturgeon coined the adage "90 per cent of everything is crud". As the Apple App Store has thousands of apps to choose from, it can be a daunting task to decide which ones to download, especially if you have to fork out your hard-earned cash.

This feature should help you fill your iPhone with apps that are useful, informative and perhaps even life-saving! To help you find 'keepers' for your iPhone, we'll give you an overview of the App Store's 20 categories and highlight five 'must-have apps' from each one.

We'll unveil apps to keep you occupied and entertained, apps that turn reluctant cooks into credible chefs, apps that let non-musicians make sweet sounds, and apps to give you local knowledge even if you're in a strange neighbourhood. Having the right apps on your iPhone can transform your life in many ways, so read on to discover which ones we recommend and why.

Essential apps

■ The computer generated illustrations are beautifully rendered and lit – just like the *Shrek* movies

Books

■ You can choose to read the book yourself or it will read for you

Before we owned an iPhone, planning our holiday reading could be a bit of a dilemma. We'd need enough books to keep us occupied while lounging on a sunbed for a week or two, but were limited by what we could cram into our suitcase. This reduced our reading list to a few paperbacks. Thanks to today's electronic book apps we can download hundreds of books onto our iPhone without eating into our luggage's weight or space allowance! This gives us more than enough material to read on the plane, before bed and on the beach. Indeed the holiday will be over before we can finish our downloaded novels. When it comes to books there's an app for everyone. You can download your favourite author's latest epic, catch up on the classics for free and keep the tiny tots entertained with illustrated storybooks. There are even comic book apps to keep teenagers happy! Read on…

"Hundreds of books without eating into luggage weight"

■ Peruse the adventures of Doctors past and present

■ Zoom in on the art in Doctor Who Comics

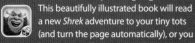

■ Search your library to find a specific book in iBooks

■ The Kindle Store provides a huge range of books

■ Guided View makes it easier to enjoy art and text on a small screen in Comics

Business

Your iPhone isn't just for playing games or reading books – it means Business too! There's a whole category on the App Store dedicated to turning your iPhone into a valuable business tool. Time is money, so we've highlighted five essential apps that will speed up typical work chores like calculating postage costs. There are apps that will turn your speech into text, enabling you to write out an email to a colleague more quickly. If you're looking for a change of career then there's an app to help you hunt out a new job. There are even apps that enable you to work out the cost of a particular parcel, so that you can avoid long queues at the post office. You can also turn your iPhone into a scanner that automatically crops and enhances the scanned image. Our essential apps will enable you to spend less time in the office and more time at play.

"Spend less time in the office and more time at play"

■ There's a keyboard to correct mistakes in Dragon Dictation

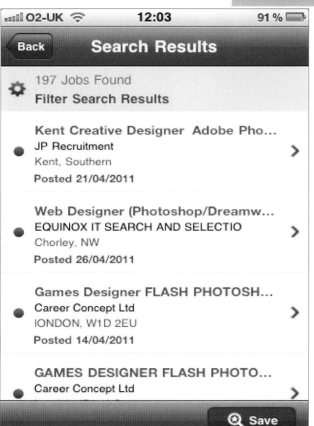

■ Filter your results by a variety of useful criteria in Monster Jobs

■ See how far your money will stretch on holiday with Unit Converter Pro

■ Email from Dragon Dictation in a couple of taps

■ Calculate the cost of posting an item via the Post Office to anywhere in the world with UK Postage Calc

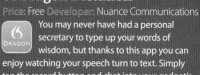

5 essential apps

01 Dragon Dictation

Price: Free Developer: Nuance Communications

You may never have had a personal secretary to type up your words of wisdom, but thanks to this app you can enjoy watching your speech turn to text. Simply tap the record button and chat into your gadget's microphone. If it makes mistakes, then you can summon the keyboard and fine-tune. Once you've created some text then it's a doddle to send it to Facebook or Twitter with a tap. With practise this app could be a genuine time-saver.

02 Monster Jobs

Price: Free Developer: Monster Worldwide

For over a decade Monster.com has been a popular place to find employment, and you could try searching its enormous database via your Safari app. However, it can be a bit fiddly to navigate around the website on an iPhone's small screen. This app's iPhone-friendly icons (like Job Search) give you easier access to search fields like Job Title. You can fine-tune your search using Keywords and Location and then peruse results formatted to fit your device's screen.

03 Genius Scan+

Price: £1.79/$2.99 Developer: The Grizzly Labs

This cool app turns your iPhone into a scanner, enabling you to take shots of valuable documents like your passport, so you can at least recover your details if you lose your passport on holiday. Unlike the iPhone's default Camera app, Genius Scan will automatically crop the scanned document to make a tidier image. It will even let you sync it with Dropbox so that you have access to a copy of the document even if you lose your phone!

04 UK Postage Calc

Price: £0.59/$0.99 Developer: John ZL

If you have a parcel or letter to post you could waste time queuing at the Post Office to get it weighed. Alternatively weigh it at work and use this handy app to calculate the cost of postage. You can then buy stamps from a machine and avoid the queues!

05 Unit Converter Pro

Price: £0.59/$0.99 Developer: Concrete Software

There are many different ways to measure distance, weight and volume, so this useful app is a must have. It's not pretty to look at but it is packed with a wide range of categories to convert – some of them very specialist! It boasts a currency converter too. A comprehensive converter!

Essential apps

5 essential apps

01 PayPal
Price: Free **Developer:** PayPal

 If you buy or sell goods on eBay you'll probably have a PayPal account, as this is one of the easiest ways to pay for goods. PayPal is also an easy way to get paid by overseas clients. The PayPal app enables you to access your PayPal account without using the Safari web browser. As it's formatted for your device's screen you can quickly see your current balance and transfer money to another PayPal user (or your own linked bank account) with ease. A good-looking and smoothly functioning financial app.

02 Fuel Cost
Price: £0.59/$0.99 **Developer:** Daniel Anderton

If you're trying to work out if it's cheaper to drive to a destination or take the train, then this app should help you make an informed choice. You can calculate how many miles your car gets to the gallon and work out the amount of fuel needed for a particular journey. This will help you realise how economical your car is to run. The app supports UK and US measurements and distances so it'll travel well.

03 iCurrency Pad
Price: £0.59/$0.99 **Developer:** Sollico

 It's easy to lose out when converting your cash for a trip abroad, but this app's up-to-date exchange rates will help you know when you're getting a good deal. With over 150 currencies to compare you should find what you need, though the Favourites section helpfully narrows down your choice to the most commonly used currencies. The app is slickly designed too, and you can swipe to change a currency with ease.

04 XpenseTracker
Price: £2.99/$4.99 **Developer:** Silverware Software

If you're on a tight budget, then XpenseTracker should help keep you on track. Label each transaction by tapping on a suitable category icon, like Car Rental or Fuel for example. These icons are especially handy if you have to file your own tax expenses, so this app could save you time and stress.

05 ATM Hunter
Price: Free **Developer:** MasterCard

If you're strapped for cash on a night out, then quickly locate and replenish your wallet with a trip to a local cash machine. The app uses your iPhone's GPS feature to display cash points by proximity. You can display the ATM machine's location on a map to make it easier to visit.

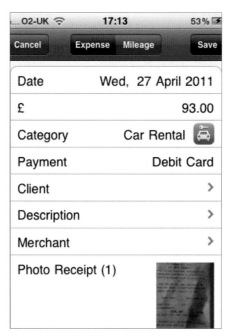

■ You can even attach photos of receipts in Xpense Tracker

Finance

In these tight times it pays to watch your pennies – and you can do that with help from these essential apps from the iTunes Finance category. They will help you avoid being ripped off when converting your currency for a trip abroad or enable you to work out how expensive a road trip will be when filling up your car with petrol. We'll also feature apps designed to help you keep track of your daily expenses, so that you can enjoy spending money while keeping your account safely in the black. There are also apps that allow you to send or request money wherever you are from the convenience of your iPhone's screen, or locate a nearby cash dispenser if you're in the mood to splash out some of your hard-earned dosh. As a bonus, many of these fab Finance apps won't cost you a penny.

■ Send cash to other PayPal users via their email address

■ Discover how much fuel your journey will require in Fuel Cost

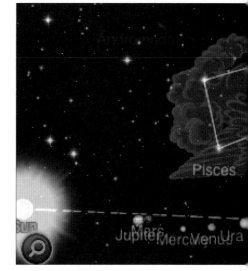

■ Learn how to identify constellations with ease in Star Walk

■ Learn more about the Hubble telescope and the universe it is observing

Education

The iPhone is the perfect platform to help you develop your knowledge of a wide range of subjects. Regardless of your age, there's an app to suit everyone. Babies can be stimulated by simple cause and effect when they tap the screen to trigger pictures and relevant sound effects – and we'll show you the perfect app to do just that! Toddlers can be entertained and educated by story-telling apps that they can interact with by triggering animations with a tap or swipe. Seasoned stargazers can use apps to identify stars and constellations in the night sky or explore the wonders of the universe via images of space captured by the orbiting Hubble telescope. We'll also share an app that will help you function more effectively abroad by giving you an understanding of a foreign language.

5 essential apps

01 Star Walk

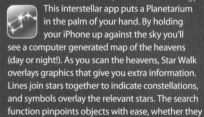

Price: £1.79/$2.99 Developer: Vito Technology

This interstellar app puts a Planetarium in the palm of your hand. By holding your iPhone up against the sky you'll see a computer generated map of the heavens (day or night!). As you scan the heavens, Star Walk overlays graphics that give you extra information. Lines join stars together to indicate constellations, and symbols overlay the relevant stars. The search function pinpoints objects with ease, whether they are distant planets or orbiting satellites.

02 Wheels on the Bus

Price: £0.59/$0.99 Developer: Duck Duck Moose

This interactive songbook features characters and objects that react to a toddler's tap. As the title song is sung, kids can push the school bus along the screen with their fingers, swipe to open the doors or poke various characters to make them jump! This app will keep your little ones entertained.

03 Sound Touch

Price: £1.79/$2.99 Developer: SoundTouch

Sound Touch encourages babies to interact with your iPhone. The screen features illustrations of various animals. When a little finger taps on a particular icon a photo and sound effect of that animal fills the screen. The photos and sound effects vary, so you can see several different types of bear for example. This is a great way to make a baby aware of various animals and objects.

04 HubbleSite

Price: Free Developer: Stsci

The Hubble Space Telescope has been snapping away at the stars for 20 years. This app shares some of the awe-inspiring images that it has captured. You can plunder this amazing collection for beautiful wallpaper and learn about the science behind the Hubble's mission.

05 AccelaStudy

Price: £5.99/$9.99 Developer: Renkara Media

You can purchase AccelaStudy apps that cover a range of languages including Turkish or Italian. Flashcards introduce you to various words and you hear how to pronounce them. You can practise identifying words via multiple choice quizzes. This is a great way to boost your foreign language vocabulary!

■ Each screen has an interactive element. Here you can swipe the wipers!

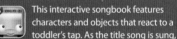

■ Record your own version to sing to your kids in the Wheels on the Bus app

■ Clicking an icon triggers sounds and pictures in Sound

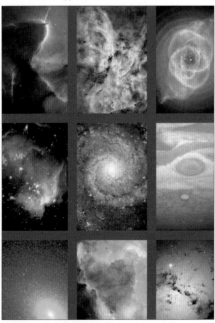

■ Wallpapers of the wonders of the universe in HubbleSite

■ Click the play button to launch a programme in the BBC iPlayer ■ Scroll through a grid of today's channels in TVGuide.co.uk

Entertainment

Thanks to your ever-present iPhone there's no danger that you'll get bored on long journeys (or when sitting on the loo!), especially if you pack it with essential apps from the Entertainment category of the App Store. You can use apps to help you keep tabs on what's on the telly so that you don't miss a thing, or enjoy interactive TV spin-off apps featuring your favourite characters. You can entertain family and friends with a variety of funny or even scary apps. In the following section we'll show you apps that record your speech and place your words in the mouths of cute animated characters. If that's too twee, then discover what a friend will look like as a bloodthirsty zombie (and post the results on Facebook!). As an alternative, see what's worth watching at your local cinema. Whatever your entertainment tastes there should be something here to keep you occupied.

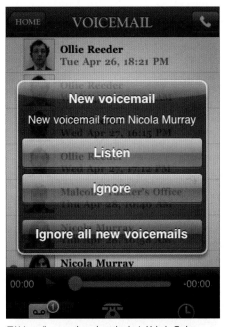

■ Find out what's showing, when it's showing and where in Flixter ■ Modify the pitch and speed to change the voice in SmackTalk ■ Voicemails appear throughout the day in Malcolm Tucker

5 essential apps

01 ZombieBooth: 3D Zombifier
Price: £0.59/$0.99
Developer: MotionPortrait

 Sometimes an app will come along that makes you go 'wow'. Zombies are enjoying a bit of a cultural high at the moment. This app lets you take a snapshot of a mate, and then applies the photo to an animated 3D model of a gruesome zombie. Each 3D zombie has the same blood-soaked teeth, but it also boasts recognisable features.

02 Malcolm Tucker: The Missing Phone
Price: £1.79/$2.99
Developer: Faber and Faber

 The award-winning comedy *The Thick Of It* (and the movie *In The Loop*) features the potty-mouthed politician Malcolm Tucker. This expletive-filled spin-off app converts your iPhone into Malcolm's lost phone. But be warned – Malcolm wants his phone back so you'll receive some colourful text messages! This app is not for those under 17.

03 SmackTalk!
Price: £0.59/$0.99
Developer: Marcus Satellite

 This is a voice-changing app that takes your phrases, records them and immediately plays them back through the mouth of a hamster, puppy or kitten. The creatures' mouths are animated and the voices cute. Be prepared for a feedback giggle loop as your friends laugh at the animals, causing the animals to laugh back! It should keep anyone amused and entertained.

04 Flixter
Price: Free
Developer: Flixster

 Wherever you are in the country, this app will use your iPhone's GPS feature to find the current films showing at your nearest cinemas (which you can locate using Maps). If you're stuck for inspiration about what to see, view trailers and read reviews of a particular film so you can avoid wasting money (or wait for the DVD release). A must-have app for film fans!

05 TVGuide.co.uk
Price: Free
Developer: acrossair

 There are many TV guides dedicated to different countries. This one covers the UK's terrestrial, satellite and Freeview channels. You can view what's on now or next, or display a grid of the day's viewing. To see shows that are available via the BBC iPlayer simply click on an adjacent play icon to load them up.

5 essential apps

01 iStunt2 - Snowboard
Price: £0.59/$0.99
Developer: Miniclip.com

 iStunt2 enables you to speed down hills on your snowboard and catch some air as you fly off ramps. While you're airborne you can snatch extra points by grabbing the board, though be careful to let go of the board before you land. For a safe landing you need to tilt the phone so that the snowboard touches down at the right angle. This game gets very challenging.

02 Wild West Pinball
Price: £0.59/$0.99
Developer: 000 Gameprom

 Wild West Pinball lets you view the entire table or pinch to zoom in on the action using Live Camera mode. The physics of the game are perfect – the ball moves at a realistic speed and the force of gravity is present and correct. Flip the ball to unlock a safe, rob a bank and even take out an opponent in a gunfight. This addictive game is worth much more than 59p!

03 Angry Birds
Price: £0.59/$0.99
Developer: Clickgamer.com

 This entertaining platform and puzzle game deserves a place on every iPhone. Use a catapult to fire a variety of birds through the air to topple objects and kill enemies hiding behind them. Different birds have different abilities – tap on a bird to make it speed up or even explode. Be warned – its combination of addictive play and high production values can eat your spare time up.

04 Tetris
Price: £0.59/$0.99
Developer: Electronic Arts

 This simple but addictive puzzle game has been around for years, but the iPhone is the perfect place to play it. Arrange falling blocks so that they complete a line and vanish. If you can't get the shapes to fit then the lines start to build up until you run out of space. While the gameplay is simple, it can get a lot harder as you aim to beat your personal best – a truly classic game.

05 Tap Zoo
Price: Free
Developer: Pocket Gems, Inc

 Fancy owning and managing your own zoo? Then this is the app for you! Buy virtual animals, breed them and build your collection over time. Your animals generate revenue which you can feed back into the zoo, though to speed things up you can buy coins using real money via the App Store.

■ Go online in Tap Zoo to visit neighbouring zoos

Games

The iPhone is a gamer's dream come true. Its high-quality screen displays pixels perfectly so you can enjoy a game's colours and graphics to the full. It's more than capable of pushing pixels around at a decent frame rate so the action never falters. Unlike traditional handheld consoles, iPhone games are relatively cheap (or even free for lite 'try before you buy' versions), so you'll never be short of games to enjoy. Gameplay varies dramatically, from first-person shooters to exhilarating sports platform games. The iPhone's touch screen makes it possible to play games without a joypad – and many apps make good use of this feature. Some games also put the iPhone's accelerometer to good use so that you can steer characters by simply tilting the phone. Whatever style of game you favour there's sure to be something to take your fancy in our essential roundup.

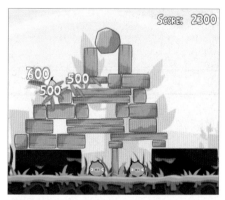

■ Tilt your iPhone to land at the correct angle in iStunt2

■ Choose a speed and angle to launch your Angry Bird…

■ …and send him crashing into the enemy's towers to earn points

Health & Fitness

We all make plans to stay fitter and thinner at various times (especially in the new year with resolutions to be made), though our motivation often runs out of steam. However, with the right apps on your iPhone you should be able to see a real change in your fitness level each day. For starters there are apps designed to help you to record and reduce your calorie intake, enabling you to lose weight at a pace that suits you, as well as highlighting flaws in your current diet. We'll even show you how to turn your iPhone

into a pedometer so you can record how many calories you've burned during your day-to-day life. In case of accidents you can turn to apps for advice, and perform life-saving first aid if necessary. Need a symptom diagnosed? We can recommend an app for that too. Needless to say our essential apps will provide you with guidance and advice, but they're no substitute for seeing a professional in a medical emergency. Get these apps on your iPhone today – they might just change your life.

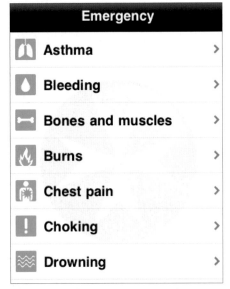

■ Discover how to deal with common emergencies by tapping the appropriate heading in the St John Ambulance app

■ You can pause your walk by double tapping on the screen to unlock it in Pocket Pedometer

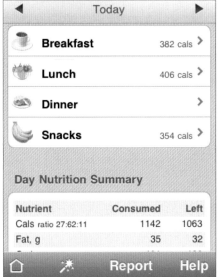

■ Discover how many more snacks you can scoff without blowing your calorie budget thanks to Calorie Counter Pro

5 essential apps

01 All-in Fitness
Price: £1.19/$1.99
Developer: ARAWELLA CORPORATION

To help us keep motivated we all need a personal trainer – and this app can turn your iPhone into just that! Kick off by entering your size and weight and choosing an area that you want to focus on. The app will then design a workout just for you. You can view photo or video examples of the recommended exercises.

02 WebMD
Price: Free
Developer: WebMD

WebMD pops a doctor into your iPhone. Tap on a body part to kick off the consultancy, then answer questions about your symptoms. The symptom checker needs a connection to the web, but a useful first aid list is stored on the iPhone for instant advice if you have to deal with an accident. On the downside the Local Health Listings search feature doesn't work in the UK.

03 Calorie Counter Pro
Price: £2.39/$3.99
Developer: 4Technologies Corporation

This app is a pleasure to use because it's relatively easy to discover the calories of the food you've consumed and you can see at a glance how many calories remain from your daily allowance. As the food database is online there can be a short lag. You can delve deeper and discover the nutritional value of the food you've eaten too.

04 St John Ambulance First Aid
Price: £1.79/$2.99
Developer: St John Ambulance

In a medical emergency you need an app that is easy to use and one that explains things clearly. This app lists typical emergencies alphabetically. Tap to see step-by-step (and often illustrated) techniques on how to help. Every iPhone needs a first aid kit like this.

05 Pocket Pedometer
Price: £0.59/$0.99
Developer: Edward Chapkis

As well as counting calories, with Calorie Counter Pro, you can keep tabs on the calories that you burn off. It uses your iPhone's accelerometer to monitor your movement as you walk, then converts this information into the number of steps taken (and the calories burned).

■ Illustrations help you give the correct treatment in this First Aid app

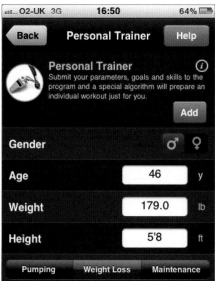

■ Input your details for a tailor-made programme in All-in Fitness

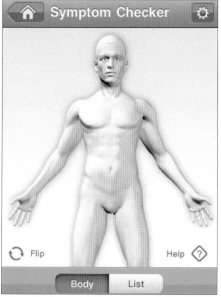

■ Click on a body part to hone down your list of symptoms in WebMD

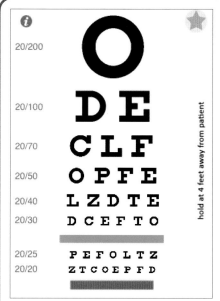

■ The smallest letters that you can read give you a visual acuity reading (like 20/30) in Eye Chart HD

Medical

The Medical category of the App Store contains apps that complement the ones in the Health & Fitness section, so you're spoiled for choice when it comes to finding apps to help you stay fit and well. It's all very well counting calories and doing workouts down the gym, but your hard work can be undone if you drink too much booze – so for that reason we've popped an alcohol unit measuring app into our medical 'must-have' list. We've also chosen apps to help you monitor common properties like blood pressure and asthma symptoms. If you can't remember when (or if) you've taken your daily medication, then there's an app for that too – so your iPhone will give you a nudge when it's time to take your medicine. You can even check out your eyesight (and discover if you're colour blind!) with a portable eye chart app.

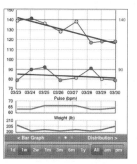

■ Display your various BP readings as colour-coded charts

■ Enter all the drugs you take and set up reminders in Dosecast

01 Dosecast
Price: Free Developer: Montuno Software, LLC

Although this app is listed as free, you do have to make an in-app purchase of £2.39 to unlock its most useful features. If you have a variety of different medications to juggle, you can easily forget which ones you've taken. This app enables you to set up alarms to remind you what drug to take and when. It will even remind you when to renew your prescription, so you won't get caught out without important drugs.

02 AsthmaMD
Price: Free Developer: Mobile Breeze

Asthma can come and go depending on factors like seasonal allergies, but when experiencing an attack you can measure your lungs' efficiency by blowing into a Peak Flow Meter. This app enables you to enter these Peak Flow readings into your iPhone. It then produces a chart showing any improvement or deterioration. You can show these charts to your doctor to help them modify your medication if necessary.

03 Alcohol Units Calculator
Price: £0.59/$0.99
Developer: Essence Computing

It's easy to exceed the Government's recommended weekly intake for alcohol consumption, but the amount you drink can have a huge influence on your long term health. If you know a drink's Alcohol by Volume % then the app will tell you how many units are in a drink. You can then log how many units you drink per week and give your liver an easier job.

04 iBP Blood Pressure
Price: £0.59/$0.99 Developer: Leading Edge Apps

This useful app enables you to log your regular blood pressure readings in your iPhone and then presents them to you (or your doctor) as graphs. It also colour codes the graphs to help you analyse different readings, so you can see when your blood pressure is normal or if you are suffering from hypertension.

05 Eye Chart HD
Price: Free Developer: Dok LLC

Eye Chart HD is no substitute for a visit to the optician, as it won't calculate your prescription or diagnose diseases like glaucoma. However it does provide an easy way to test your visual acuity. Simply fire up the eye chart, pop your iPhone four feet away and try and read the smallest letters.

5 essential apps

01 The Photo Cookbook

Price: £2.99/$4.99 Developer: ditter. projektagentur Gmb

The Photo Cook Book – Quick and Easy does what it says on the tin! If you want to develop some culinary skills, then the lavishly illustrated Photo Cookbook is a must have. This educational app is packed full of recipes that guide you step-by-step. There's a wide range of dishes and desserts to create. You can also refer to a photo of a meal's raw ingredients when you're out shopping, so that you don't miss a thing!

02 iMapMyWalk+

Price: £2.99/$4.99 Developer: MapMyFitness

You may have several different routes that you can take to work or into town. By using this app you can log each route and discover which is the shortest. It will even tell you how high you've ascended. If you're walking to be healthy you can track the calories that you've burned and view statistics like your average walking speed. This essential app will give you more motivation to get out and about.

03 eBay Mobile

Price: Free Developer: eBay Inc

If you're a keen eBay user then this app is all you need to keep track of your online auctions. It's formatted for your iPhone screen, so whether you're buying or selling you can find the information you need with ease. It can be a chore to leave feedback on multiple auctions or mark items as having been dispatched. Thanks to this fab app you can perform these tedious tasks on the move and stay on top of your eBay admin.

04 AroundMe

Price: Free Developer: Tweakersoft

Every iPhone needs an app that displays local amenities, and this one does the job effectively. Scroll through a list of categories (like Parking) and see a list of all the options (with the closest listed first). A quick tap will show the location on a map in relation to your own position.

05 Pimp Your Screen

Price: £0.59/$0.99 Developer: Apalon

This colourful app enables you to add distinctive-looking designs to your iPhone's home or background screens. Alternatively you can use it to add icon skins that display your apps in eye-catching ways. A great way to make your iPhone stand out from the crowd!

Lifestyle

The Lifestyle category of the iTunes store contains apps covering a diverse range of subjects. If you're keen on getting out and about (whether that's through walking or cycling), then you can use apps to map your favourite routes and discover how long a particular journey is in miles. While on a stroll you can fire up apps to help you discover local amenities (like pubs or restaurants), or check out the status of your eBay auctions when you're on the move. We also feature an app that enables you to personalise your iPhone's home screen, so that you can add creative-looking shelves for your Lifestyle apps to sit on. If you want to conquer your lack of cooking skills then we have a must-have app that will enable you to impress family and friends with newfound cooking skills. Whatever your lifestyle, these apps should make a difference.

"Whatever lifestyle, these apps should make a difference"

■ Pimp Your Screen to display app icons in creative ways

■ A photo and description of every ingredient in a recipe helps you get prepared in The Photo Cookbook

■ Scroll through lots of tasty looking themed recipes – from vegetarian to fish dishes

■ Browse through themed categories in Pimp Your Screen to find a new look

■ Display the location of your search on a map in the AroundMe app

5 essential apps

01 MorphWiz
Price: £5.99/$9.99
Developer: Wizdom Music, LLC

 If you lack musical experience but fancy making sounds, then MorphWiz could be the perfect app. Slide your fingers across the screen to produce a range of synthesised sounds and enjoy light effects radiating from your fingertips. There's no need to wade through lots of instructions before making sounds.

02 djay for iPhone
Price: £0.59/$0.99
Developer: algoriddim

 This app is amazing – it looks lovely and functions fabulously. It places two vinyl turntables on your iPhone's screen. You can place tracks from your iTunes library onto each turntable and play the tracks as if they were vinyl. A fader enables you to mix the two records together to create something new. You can mix live, or record and share your mix with mates.

03 TuneIn Radio Pro
Price: £0.59/$0.99
Developer: Synsion Radio Technologies

 Most radio stations these days also broadcast via the web, which is why TuneIn Radio Pro can find any radio station. You can set up a list of favourite stations and if something takes your fancy you can record. It'll even use your location to present you with a list of local stations. You'll never be short of something to listen to again!

04 Shazam
Price: Free
Developer: Shazam Entertainment Ltd.

 Hear a song you like but have no idea which band performs it? With Shazam you can whip out your iPhone, let it listen to the music and identify the track in moments. You can discover song lyrics, see album covers and download the track via iTunes. This is definitely a musical must have for every iPhone user with an interest in the latest tunes.

05 Last.fm
Price: Free
Developer: Last.fm

 Last.fm lets you choose the type of music that you like, then it feeds you similar examples in the style of your chosen artist. This is less precise than searching for a specific band or track, but it does let you rediscover old favourites and uncover new bands too. You'll need to subscribe after the free 50-track trial.

Music

If you love listening to music, or even want to make it, then the following essential apps deserve a place on your iPhone. We'll feature an amazing app that enables you to mix iPod Library's tracks together like an old-school DJ (complete with scratchy back spins that you can produce by swiping the iPhone's screen!). Alternatively you may want to simply stroke the screen to generate synthesized sounds and create a relaxing ambient soundscape – there's an app for that too! If you'd rather consume music than create it, then there's an app that will tell you the track and artist that you're listening to by sampling it through your iPhone's mic, so you won't miss out on discovering new bands. You can rediscover old music too by listening to music-streaming apps, and turn your iPhone into a radio that will pick up (and even record) stations from anywhere in the world.

■ Become a virtual DJ in the clever djay for iPhone app

■ Tap the screen and Shazam will quickly tag and identify the song

■ Record your favourite programmes as they stream to your iPhone in TuneIn

■ You can generate different sounds by placing multiple fingers on the screen in MorphWiz

Essential apps

5 essential apps

01 CoPilot Live

Price: £16.99/$27.99 **Developer:** ALK Technologies, LTD.

This is the most expensive app in our feature, but it's much cheaper than buying a dedicated satnav. It uses your iPhone's GPS function to help you navigate road trips. Like other satnav displays, you can see your vehicle's position on a 3D map and follow arrows that guide you. When you get to complex junctions a lane indicator keeps you on track. It's worth buying a hands-free mount holder so you don't get distracted holding your gadget.

02 Layar Reality Browser

Price: Free **Developer:** Layar B.V.

Instead of using a 2D map to find local points of interest, try a bit of augmented reality! Layar works by allowing you to search for a particular amenity (like a coffee shop). Instead of displaying the search results as icons on a 2D map it overlays them on your iPhone's live camera image. As you pan the phone to view a location you'll see floating icons or images that represent the locations of your search results.

03 Trails – GPS tracker

Price: £2.39/$3.99 **Developer:** Felix Lamouroux

If you're a big fan of hiking then this app will let you record your adventures using the iPhone's GPS facility. You can snap photos of interesting sights along the way and create waypoints to mark points of interest. Cyclists should find this app useful to as it can display the topography of the terrain. You can also download maps before you set out in case the iPhone can't get a signal on your journey.

04 ForeverMap

Price: £1.19/$2.99 **Developer:** skobbler GmbH

If you're travelling abroad it can cost a fortune to download map details using the standard Maps app. ForeverMap lets you download a country or city's map before you travel so you can avoid excessive data roaming charges. You can then use the downloaded map to plan routes and discover points of interest.

05 Plane Finder

Price: £2.99/$4.99 **Developer:** pinkfroot limited

This fascinating real-time plane-tracking app is a real eye-opener, as you can see just how full our skies are with aircraft. If your friends or family are travelling by air you can follow their progress by searching for their flight number. An essential app for any flight enthusiast. There's a cut-down free version available too.

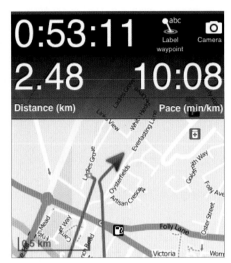

■ Add waypoints and assign photos as you hike. You can pause the tracking at any time in Trails

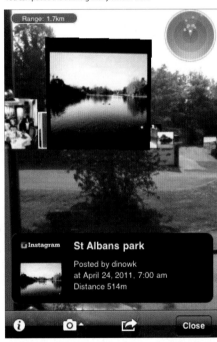

■ Pan your iPhone to discover the direction of local points of interest (POI) in Layars

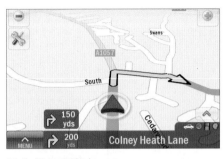

■ In the 3D view CoPilot shows you which turn to take to get home safely

■ Find lots of information about your location by tapping on an icon

Navigation

We tend to carry our iPhone around with us at all times, so it's the perfect device to help us get where we want to go, or find local amenities like pubs or hotels. Your iPhone already comes with a decent built-in Maps app that does a great job of showing you how to get from A to B – but there are other apps that can extend and expand your gadget's navigational abilities in exciting ways. In this section we'll introduce you to five essential navigation apps that perform a variety of different functions. One of them even transforms your iPhone into a turn-by-turn navigator at the fraction of the price of a dedicated gadget like a TomTom satnav – just make sure you use it safely in the car. You can also keep tabs on the flight paths of specific planes, or discover the location of local points of interest by panning the iPhone's camera around the area you are in.

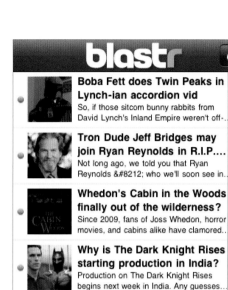

blastr

Boba Fett does Twin Peaks in Lynch-ian accordion vid
So, if those sitcom bunny rabbits from David Lynch's Inland Empire weren't off-...

Tron Dude Jeff Bridges may join Ryan Reynolds in R.I.P....
Not long ago, we told you that Ryan Reynolds — who we'll soon see in...

Whedon's Cabin in the Woods finally out of the wilderness?
Since 2009, fans of Joss Whedon, horror movies, and cabins alike have clamored..

Why is The Dark Knight Rises starting production in India?
Production on The Dark Knight Rises begins next week in India. Any guesses...

Aliens crash the royal wedding?
MARS NEEDS ROYALS! At least that's what can be inferred from a 2 and 1/2...

Latest News — Sections — Images — Video

■ Browse Science Fiction news via sections or in chronological order

News

If you're hungry for the latest news then the iPhone is the perfect gadget to sate your appetite. We all have different interests when it comes to news, so there are specialist apps for every genre of news – like the world of science fiction for example. Most newspapers have an online edition, but that can be a fiddle to navigate using your iPhone's Safari browser. We'll take a look at a couple of the best iPhone newspaper apps to help you enjoy a decent digital version of your favourite newspaper without having to pinch to zoom in on small web browser text. There are even apps that will turn your iPhone into a newsreader, so you can listen to headlines from any news source you choose while on the move. There's even an app that enables you to stream your favourite podcasts straight to your iPhone without you having to download and sync them.

"There are specialist apps for every genre of news"

■ Enjoy news via the NYTimes app's video feed

■ News is broken up into helpful headlines that you can explore in a tap

■ Type in a greeting and choose a news feed for the Tick Talk robot to read

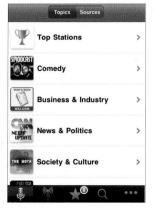

■ Browse through topics via category or search for something in Stitcher Radio

■ Enjoy your very own animated robotic newsreader with Tick Talk

5 essential apps

01 Met Office
Price: Free
Developer: Met Office

For a reliable local weather forecast it pays to go straight to the source. If you live in the UK then your region will be monitored by the Met Office. Unlike some other weather apps you don't have to manually add your location as it will use your iPhone's GPS to send you a local forecast. It also displays satellite images of current cloud conditions. Simple but effective.

02 Weather HD
Price: £0.59/$0.99
Developer: vimov, LLC

This app isn't as informative as some of the others, but it's the prettiest to look at. The current weather conditions are represented using colourful HD videos. Clouds float by, raindrops fall or the Sun rises over windblown wheat stalks. This enables the app to function as attractive moving wallpaper. There's also text to inform you of temperature, humidity and wind strength.

03 AccuWeather
Price: Free
Developer: AccuWeather, Inc.

Like other apps this one will give you a local forecast using icons, but it does have some nice touches. You can view your location on a Google Map and the app will overlay an animation of satellite-sourced cloud conditions. It also boasts a useful Lifestyle section where you can see the current weather's suitability for various activities and its effect on various medical conditions.

04 Pollen Forecast UK
Price: Free
Developer: Clarityn

Although this app is primarily designed to sell hayfever prevention tablets it's not to be sneezed at! View a forecast that uses colour-coded icons indicating pollen count intensity. A handy Allergy Calendar helps you discover what particular plant or tree you might be allergic too. There's even a store finder if you need to stock up.

05 Weather+
Price: £0.59/$0.99
Developer: International Travel Weather Calculator

If you need a weather forecast in a hurry then this app places all you need to know on a single screen. Various widgets give you time, temperature, humidity and wind strength. You can customise the screen to simplify it, so only the most useful information is visible against the background.

Weather

Most of us will just want an app that forecasts the weather in our area for the next few days – and there are plenty of apps that perform that function. Indeed you've already got a free weather forecasting app on your iPhone.

To complement the existing Weather app we have trawled through the App Store for apps that will bring you additional weather-related information. There's a deluge of weather-centric apps to choose from, which can make it a challenge to find which apps are essential (and which actually work!). When choosing our five essential apps we have gone for variety, to make sure that all your weather-related needs will be covered. You'll then know when to reach for the umbrella or a tube of suntan lotion.

We've gone for apps that display the forecasts as attractive weather-themed videos, apps that display satellite cloud maps plus apps that give you more specialist forecasts like pollen counts.

■ You can simplify information in Weather+ for a clean look

■ This app crams lots of information into a single screen

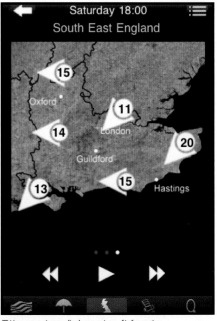

■ You can swipe to display a variety of information, from temperature to wind strength from the Met Office

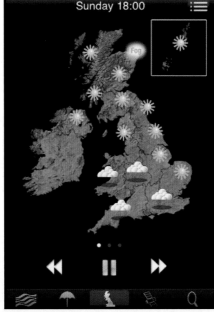

■ Press the play icon to view predicted weather conditions for the next few days from the Met Office

■ View the forecasts daily or hourly in Weather HD

■ Get a flavour of the weather in an instant in Weather HD

■ There are video forecasts to enjoy, but most of them are American-based

Photography

Thanks to your ever-present iPhone there's no danger that you'll miss a photo (or video) opportunity. The built-in Camera app enables you to focus on your subject matter and capture a decent exposure much of the time, but there will be occasions when you may want to produce more creative-looking results. One of our essential apps enables you to turn photos into striking line drawings or paintings at the touch of a button, so you can impress your friends with your apparent artistic skills. Another of our essential apps mimics the amazing colours and tones of toy cameras, turning ordinary snapshots into extraordinary retro images with attractive borders. There's even an app to turn your digital video footage into vintage silent movie scenes, which can be great fun. But we'll kick off with an app that adds several more useful functions than you get with your basic iPhone Camera app, to help you shoot better images in the first place…

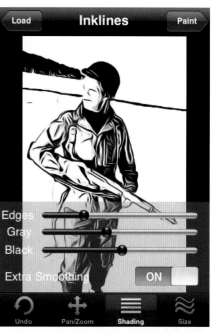

 Produce striking shifts in colour, rich tones and arty borders in a tap with the wonderful Hipstamatic

 Turn complex photos into simple line art images with ToonPAINT

 Photo Transfer also needs to be installed on the receiving device

5 essential apps

01 Ultimate Camera
Price: £0.59/$0.99
Developer: MacPhun, LLC

When shooting on the standard iPhone camera you need to tap on the little camera icon to capture a shot. If you miss this small button then you may miss an important moment. Ultimate Camera's Big Button mode enables you to capture a shot by tapping anywhere on the screen (which is great for shooting self-portraits on the 3GS, as it lacks the front camera of iPhone 4).

02 Hipstamatic
Price: £1.19/$1.99
Developer: Synthetic Corp

This fantastic app will motivate you to shoot many more images thanks to the striking results. It mimics the look produced by cheap plastic toy film cameras and adds image artefacts like light leakage, uneven exposure, shifts in colour and borders. You can swap lenses or film types to experiment, or shake the iPhone to try a random lens/film combination

03 Silent Film Director
Price: £0.59/$0.99
Developer: MacPhun, LLC

Turn home movies into vintage clips with this app. It post-processes your clips and converts them into mono with added film scratches, or you can go for the desaturated colours of Seventies home video. You can assign different sound effects (like an old movie projector) or music tracks for added authenticity.

04 ToonPAINT
Price: £1.19/1.99
Developer: Toon-FX

This clever app turns photos from your iPhone into stylised line art, like the sample in the app icon. You can then use your finger to sample colours from the original photo and paint over the image to produce a work of art. You can tweak the shading and brush tip size and zoom in to paint the fiddly bits. It might not be practical, but it is fun!

05 Photo Transfer App
Price: £1.79/$2.99
Developer: Enrique Rodriguez

If you have an iPad then you may prefer to edit your photos using the larger screen, but it can be time-consuming syncing your iPhone to your home computer and then transferring the images. This useful app enables you to send photos directly to your iPad via Wi-Fi.

Essential apps

5 essential apps

01 2Do

Price: £3.99/$6.99 Developer: Guided Ways
Technologies Ltd

 One way to keep organised is to write a
list and cross tasks out as they're done.
Unlike some free apps, 2Do enables you
to group various tasks into different calendars. You
can also prioritise tasks so that the most urgent
ones are at the top. You can even assign notes and
pictures and add practical actions that let you call
or mail a contact in a click. Add an alarm and you'll
receive a notification when it needs to be done.

02 Dropbox

Price: Free Developer: Dropbox

 There are plenty of file-sharing apps, but
Dropbox stands out from the crowd. The
free service gives you a Dropbox folder
on your computer and one on your iPhone. When
you drag a file into your computer's Dropbox
it's automatically uploaded to an online folder,
enabling you to view the file using the iPhone. You
can pay to increase the 2GB storage capacity. A fast
and effective file-sharing app.

03 MobileMe iDisk

Price: Free Developer: Apple

 If you're a member of Apple's MobileMe
service then you'll also have an iDisk. Like
Dropbox, iDisk is an online storage cloud.
The iDisk app enables you to view clips, browse
photos and read documents. Because you have to
subscribe to be a MobileMe member, your iDisk
gives you a whopping 20GB to play with compared
with Dropbox's 2GB.

04 My Desk

Price: £1.79/$2.99 Developer: Metabrain
Corporation

 Now your iPhone's desktop can be as
cluttered and personalised as your home
or office desk. This app scatters a coffee
cup and wind-up toy on your virtual desktop plus
more useful things like a To Do list, a clock, a photo
frame slide-show, an iTunes controller and even a
live Twitter feed!

05 Keynote Remote

Price: £0.59/$0.99 Developer: Apple

 Keynote is software that lets you show
images and graphs on your laptop.
Impress your colleagues during a
presentation by whipping out your iPhone and
advancing the slides by swiping your finger. You
can also access presenter notes on your iPhone to
help you keep tabs on your presentation's content.

Productivity

Thanks to apps, your iPhone can be many things.
It has the power to become a communications
device, a camera or even a games console. It
can also help you get things done in the home
or in your office thanks to a range of essential
Productivity apps. In this section we'll show you
apps that enable you to access (and even share)
important documents while you're out of the
office, so you're no longer chained to your desk.

Indeed we've even included a mobile desktop
app for your iPhone (complete with family photo
and obligatory cup of coffee) so you can pretend
you're at work when you're out and about. If you're
a MobileMe user then you can access your iDisk
from your iPhone too and even use your device to
remote control a Keynote presentation and impress
your work colleagues. Here's a run down of those
essential productivity apps…

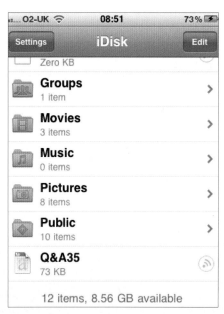

■ Store up to 20GB of videos, photos or text documents on your
iDisk (which is more than you can fit on your iPhone)

■ You can shoot images on your iPhone and upload them to the
Dropbox, then email a link so that others can access the files

Reference

We all take the internet for granted as a source of information, and the iPhone is often the portal we use when we need to access the world wide web's ocean of knowledge. Although the Safari app's Google search field is often our first port of call looking for information, it can take a while to wade through hundreds of results before we find what we're after. The apps featured in this section should help you narrow down your search to find relevant information more quickly, whether it's crime statistics for your hometown or the missing link in your family tree. We've also included the obligatory augmented reality app, so that you can discover which direction to walk in to find local points of interest while looking through your iPhone's camera! Our essential reference apps should help you filter your search for information more effectively.

■ Search categories in Augmented Reality Browser

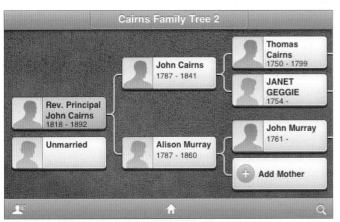
■ Browse your family trees while on the move in Ancestry

■ Edit and modify individual entries at any time

5 essential apps

01 Augmented Reality Browser
Price: Free
Developer: acrossair

 This app makes it a doddle to navigate to local points of interest. Browse for the usual things like Coffee, Banks or Museums by tapping on search categories. You'll then see results overlaid on the feed from your iPhone's camera. Pan the camera to discover the search result's distance and direction, then start walking!

02 Google Search
Price: Free
Developer: Google

 We all take Google for granted when searching via Safari, but this dedicated Google app makes it even easier to find things fast. Instead of typing into a fiddly Search field you can speak to the app and it will turn speech to text. The latest version of the app has a visual search option too. Take a photo of a barcode, for example, and Google will hunt out information for you.

03 Crime Map UK
Price: Free
Developer: Ravensoft

 There's something exciting about viewing a map of your hometown and being able to pinpoint the location of recent crimes. This knowledge helps you feel streetwise, even if the precise details of the crimes in question aren't available. You can also see an overview of all the crimes in your area and see how the crime rate compares to the average.

04 Dictionary.com
Price: Free
Developer: Dictionary.com, LLC

 They say it pays to enrich your word power – and this app will do just that. As it contains around 2 million words and definitions you don't need to have internet access to look something up. You can even search for words using speech recognition (though you'll need to talk slowly and clearly for this to work).

05 Ancestry
Price: Free
Developer: Ancestry.com

If you're investigating your family tree then chances are you'll be a member of Ancestry.com. This app formats that site for your iPhone, enabling you to view or edit trees with ease and even upload photos of family heirlooms. This well-designed app provides an easy way to share family trees with relatives.

Social networking

Many of us spend more time socialising online than we do in the flesh, enabling us to sustain friendships with family, friends and colleagues over any distance. Your ever-present iPhone is a key tool in helping you keep up-to-date with your online friends. We'll take a look at apps that let you find out who's doing what, and discover apps to help you make cheap or even free calls to other iPhone users.

If you use any of the main social networking sites then you'll find dedicated apps that let you access these sites with ease. We'll take a look at the apps from big-hitters like Facebook and Twitter, and show you ways to gather different networks into a single app. As well as keeping up with the social whirl we'll also show you an app that will help you build and expand a network of business colleagues too.

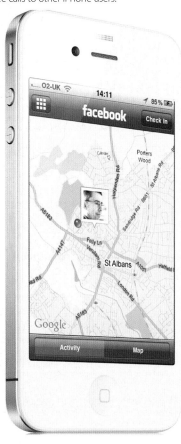

■ Check In with Places so that friends can see your position on a map in Facebook

■ Call, message or video chat with other Skype users simply and quickly

■ Click here to set up a group chat with friends on a specific network in IM+

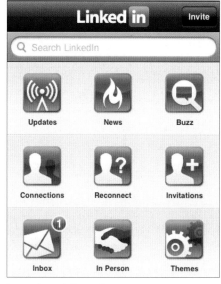

■ Keep tabs on who knows what's occurring in your professional network with LinkedIn

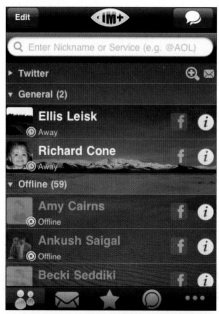

■ See the status of contacts from a variety of networks in IM+

5 essential apps

01 IM+
Price: Free Developer: SHAPE Services

 The problem with keeping track of your mates is that they may be scattered across a variety of social networking sites. Fortunately you can gather everyone together using IM+. This app is an all-in-one messenger that enables you to see who's online regardless of their preferred social network This could become your one-stop-shop when it comes to social network chats.

02 Skype
Price: Free Developer: Skype Software S.a.r.l

 Skype is an amazing app that lets you voice, text and video chat with friends who also have Skype installed on their laptop or iPhone. It does this for free, making it an essential social networking app for any iPhone. You can also make low cost calls to overseas landlines by buying Skype credits. These can automatically be updated via a feed from your PayPal account, so there's no danger of the call becoming interrupted.

03 LinkedIn
Price: Free Developer: LinkedIn Corporation

 LinkedIn is a social network resource for professionals. You can pop your CV on the site and invite existing colleagues to connect. You'll then receive suggestions of other professionals to connect with. You can also send and receive professional recommendations from colleagues to help boost your employment chances.

04 Facebook
Price: Free Developer: Facebook, Inc.

 With more than 6 million active users we probably don't need to tell you that Facebook is a popular social networking site, but if you're a Facebook addict then this app must be included on your iPhone. Update your Facebook status via your iPhone and even let people keep tabs on your recent GPS locations.

05 Twitter
Price: Free Developer: Twitter, Inc

 Do we need to tell you what Twitter is? Well, if you're back from outer space then Twitter is a site that lets you announce (or tweet) your current activity or opinion in 140 characters or less. You can tweet, or follow other users' tweets. A great way to snoop on the daily lives of others.

5 essential apps

01 Splashpath
Price: Free
Developer: Daniel Morgan

This app enables you to find a local swimming bath and motivates you to swim! Kick off by searching for your nearest pools. Check out the profiles of other Splashpath users who swim there. You can then take a swimming challenge like the Thames Bridge Swim. The app lets you log the number of pool lengths it would take to perform the challenge.

02 Bike Repair
Price: £1.79/$2.99
Developer: Atomic Softwares

Cycling can be a great way to stay fit, but if you have mechanical problems it can be expensive. Buying this app could save you a bob or two as it shows you how to diagnose and fix common faults. Solve a problem by tapping on the appropriate part. Scroll through the list of possible problems and see an illustrated step-by-step guide on how to fix the fault.

03 Tony Hawk's Lite Trick Tips
Price: Free
Developer: Epic Tilt

This app is a must have for keen skateboarders who want to emulate the skills of the legendary Tony Hawks. Scroll through the list of tricks and then read the step-by-step instructions on how to perform them. For more information watch a video of the trick being performed. A slick and well designed app that doesn't miss a trick!

04 Formula1.com 2011
Price: Free
Developer: Formula1.com

After you've registered with the Formula1.com site you can use this app to get live data straight from a race. See the current stats of your favourite drivers using live timing and even discover track wind speed and direction. There's a handy timetable too, so you can enjoy the anticipation of the next race!

05 Sky Sports News
Price: Free
Developer: BSkyB

Whatever sport you support or follow, you should discover the latest breaking news stories and match scores via this app. There are categories dedicated to a range of popular sports. You can also stream Sky Sports Radio from the app so you can hear the sporting headlines while on the go.

Sports

There are many sports and recreational activities to enjoy, so no matter what sport you're interested in, there's bound to be an app for you in our sporting must haves. We have an app that enables cyclists to save repair bills by diagnosing mechanical problems and showing them the solutions. If you're wondering which pool to swim in and need to find swimming challenges to overcome then we have an app for you too. If your interest in sport is indulged from the comfort of your armchair then we have a sport-centric news app to give you details of current and future sporting events. There's even an app that enables you to follow the live lap timings of your favourite Formula 1 driver as he speeds round the track. And if you're trying to master that Frontside 180 Ollie move on your skateboard then take a tip from Tony Hawks himself!

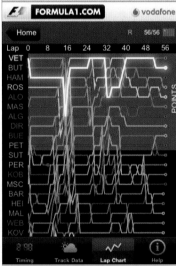

■ Data is streamed from the track in Formula1.com

■ Listen to sporting headlines with Sky Sports News

■ View a complete trick as a video clip in Tony Hawk's Lite Trick Tips

■ Break complex tricks down into manageable steps with Tony Hawks

5 essential apps

01 Kayak

Price: Free Developer: Kayak.com

 As a travel app, Kayak is a good all-rounder. It enables you to find the cheapest flight and hotel prices from the comfort of your iPhone's screen. Before heading off use its tickbox packing list to ensure that you don't forget important things. It's also a useful app when starting your journey too, as the Flight Tracker option enables you to see if you plane is going to take off as scheduled. There's even a currency converter. A traveller's must have!

02 TripAdvisor

Price: Free Developer: TripAdvisor LLC

 Holidays can be expensive and you don't get many of them, so you'll want them to be perfect. This app enables you to read reviews of hotels and restaurants from people who've already experienced them. The Things to do section is very useful as it will give you advice about various tourist attractions without the need to fork out for a guidebook. An informative travel app.

03 Wikihood

Price: Free Developer: NextAroundYou

 Wikipedia is a dauntingly large resource. Fortunately, this clever app helps you mine that mass of information to bring you interesting local knowledge. Discover nearby points of interest and read articles on famous people with a local connection. You can also view photos attached to Wikipedia entries, so no matter how long you've lived in an area you're sure to learn something new about it.

04 thetrainline

Price: Free Developer: Trainline.com Limited

 This is a great app if you simply need to find out when to arrive at the station to catch a train to your chosen destination. It saves you from just missing a train or hanging around on the platform for ages for the next on. You can also use the app to book tickets.

05 Word Lens

Price: Free Developer: Quest Visual

If you're unsure whether the Spanish label on a door means gents or ladies, take a snap of the text and let Word Lens have a go a translating it into English. However, you need to make an in-app purchase costing £5.99 before you can use the app. Doesn't work too well with ornate fonts though.

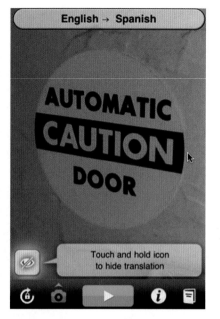

Travel

Your iPhone is the perfect travel companion, especially when packed with our selection of essential Travel apps. There are apps for every stage of your trip. Before you go, use apps to read hotel reviews from fellow travellers before making a hotel booking, or plan which places to visit when abroad by following other's recommendations. Use apps to search for the best travel deals (whether flight or car hire) and make a booking directly from your iPhone. If you're planning to travel by train we have an app to let you check out timetables and buy tickets. If you're staying at home you can use an app to take a tour of local points of interest and learn about your town's history. There's even an app that turns your iPhone's camera into a foreign text translator (though it is limited to dealing with short signs that have nice clean fonts). And it all takes up a lot less space than an A-Z and a bumper English/French phrasebook!

■ Discover relevant local landmark images in Wikihood

■ Use a list to pinpoint points of interest on a map in Wikihood

■ Find a bargain hotel and check out reviews with TripAdvisor

■ Read reviews and then find places of interest on a map

■ Find the cheapest flights and make a booking with Kayak

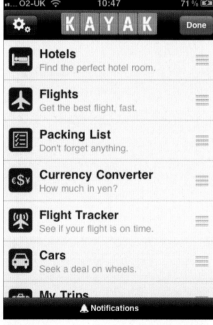
■ Tick off options on your packing list to avoid forgetting things

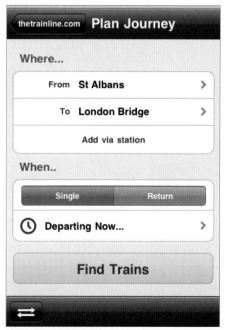
■ Plan a train trip and then make an in-app thetrainline booking

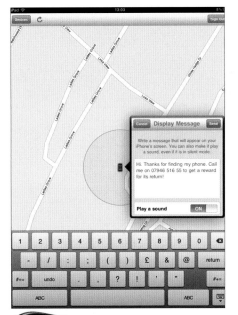

5 essential apps

01 Find My iPhone

Price: Free Developer: Apple

 If you only download one app from the Utility category then make sure that it's this one. It could save you lots of time, stress and expense (though you'll need to make sure that the Find My iPhone option is turned on in the Settings>Accounts>MobileMe menu). If you lose your iPhone, download the Find My iPhone software onto your Mac or iPad. It'll pin-point your iPhone's location on a map.

02 1Password Pro

Price: £8.99/$14.99 Developer: Agile Web Solutions

 If you find it hard to remember multiple passwords then the 1Password Pro app will help. This enables you to store passwords for accounts like bank, MobileMe or iTunes safely. It'll even log you into your password-protected websites with a tap. It may be a relatively pricey app, but if someone gets their hands on your financial data then it could cost you a lot more.

03 Perfect Photo

Price: £0.59/$0.99 Developer: MacPhun LLC

 With your ever-present iPhone you'll never be short of a photo to share, and with this app you can make sure that your images look their best. Perfect Photo puts Photoshop-style image-editing tools on your iPhone. The app's tools enable you to tweak a shot's colours and tones, remove spots and blemishes and tackle red eye.

04 Media Remote for iPhone

Price: Free Developer: Sony Corporation

 If you have a Sony Blu-ray player, then you can use your iPhone as a remote control. Both the Sony gadget and the iPhone need to be on a Wi-Fi network. Fast forward with a swipe or pause with a tap. Program the iPhone to pause playback as soon as you pick it up.

05 Alarm

Price: £0.59/$0.99 Developer: Bocker Applications

 At work you may be reluctant to leave your iPhone lying on your desk in case it gets pinched. You can use this app to set off an alarm as soon as someone touches your iPhone (and only you know the code to deactivate the noise!). It can also be triggered by sound. Very James Bond…

Utilities

Thanks to the App Store's Utilities category you can turn your iPhone into the type of gadget that James Bond would be proud to own (although he'd probably trash it before the end of the movie!). There are Utility apps that enable you to pinpoint your iPhone's location on a map and even wipe its precious data if it falls into enemy hands. If your phone is stolen then there are secure data storage apps that will keep your passwords and bank details safe from prying eyes. If you own a Sony DVD or Blu-ray player you can use apps to control your machine by swiping a finger on the iPhone's screen. And you can even leave your iPhone lying about, safe in the knowledge that a Utility app is on guard, waiting to set off an audio alarm should someone dare to pick it up. These Utility apps are licensed to thrill!

■ Use sliders to boost colour or brighten underexposed shots in Perfect Photo

■ Send a message to your missing iPhone with Find My iPhone

■ Change to a more traditional remote in Media Remote

Your questions answered
Solutions to those common iPhone problems

Can I sync my Facebook contacts?

Hard as it might be to believe, even as recently as a couple of decades ago, the means favoured by most people to keep in touch with distant friends or family was the telephone or letter. Their idea of a contact list was something you scrawled in the back of your diary – or Filofax.

Since then email and text messaging have grown in popularity and address books are more often than not held digitally.

But the blossoming of social media tools such as Twitter and Facebook into viable communication channels in their own right has complicated matters still further. Most people's network of friends is far wider than it once was. Now the problem is keeping track of everyone you know. How do you meld the contents of your iPhone's Contacts app with your Facebook Friends list?

In fact, it's possible to keep your friends list and iPhone contacts neatly in sync, and to do so you will need the Facebook app for iPhone (it's a free download). If you're only just getting into Facebook on the iPhone you may already have been given the option on first launch to synchronise your Facebook friends with your

iPhone contacts. From there you can just follow the on-screen instructions.

But if you missed that option, or if you've only just decided that you want to sync your Facebook and iPhone contacts, here's how to corral your social media contacts into one handy list in your iPhone's Contacts app.

Sync your Facebook friends to Contacts

Launch Facebook

Open the Facebook app on your iPhone and log in to your account as usual. Tap the 'Friends' icon at the top of the screen and then tap the Arrow button at the top right of the resulting window.

Sync contacts

Tap the 'Sync' button at the top of the screen. In the next window, slide the Syncing slider to On. Tap the Sync Contacts button. This starts importing your Contacts to Facebook.

Add photos

Another nifty feature when syncing your Facebook friends to Contacts is the ability to grab images from the profiles of Facebook friends to add to your iPhone contacts. Tap the Agree button.

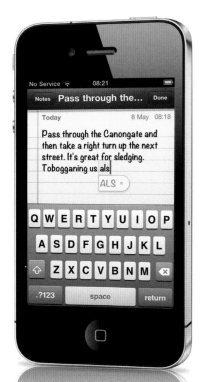

Can you turn off autocorrect?

As you type text using the iPhone's software keyboard, a small floating box often appears above the words that offers both predictive text – to complete words for you – or an alternative if it thinks you have misspelled them.

If you press 'Space' on the keyboard, the iPhone's suggested text replaces what you have typed, while if you tap the box, the text that you type is accepted as correct, and over time, the iPhone should learn the words that you use most frequently.

Autocorrect can save you a lot of time, but sometimes it's a hindrance, particularly if you're typing a lot of words that aren't in the iPhone's dictionary, and you're better off without it. In those cases, you can turn it off. Here's how.

> "Autocorrect can be a hindrance if you're typing a lot of words that aren't in the iPhone's dictionary"

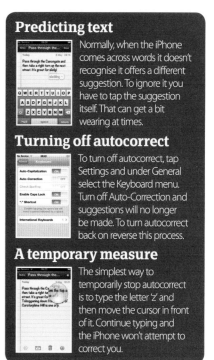

Predicting text

Normally, when the iPhone comes across words it doesn't recognise it offers a different suggestion. To ignore it you have to tap the suggestion itself. That can get a bit wearing at times.

Turning off autocorrect

To turn off autocorrect, tap Settings and under General select the Keyboard menu. Turn off Auto-Correction and suggestions will no longer be made. To turn autocorrect back on reverse this process.

A temporary measure

The simplest way to temporarily stop autocorrect is to type the letter 'z' and then move the cursor in front of it. Continue typing and the iPhone won't attempt to correct you.

How do I charge my iPhone?

You can either use the plug adapter that is packaged with your iPhone, or attach your iPhone to your computer using its USB cable and charge from that. The advantage of the latter method is that you can sync and back up your iPhone as it's charging, although that does mean your battery won't charge quite as fast.

> "Sync and back up your iPhone as it's charging"

Showing the power

The iPhone's battery indicator in the top-right corner displays approximately how much charge is left in the battery. How long that will last depends on what you are using your phone for.

Green means go

The battery normally displays a green icon while it's charging, and is fully charged when the battery icon turns completely green. You can continue to use your iPhone while it is being charged.

Low battery situation

If the battery is depleted, the red battery image indicates that the iPhone needs to charge for some time before you can use it. Plug it in and the phone will start up again after a few minutes.

Can I export documents?

There are several ways of exporting documents from your iPhone to your Mac or PC. The easiest route is to simply email the documents to yourself at an account you can access from your computer.

Some apps link to online storage services, such as Dropbox (www.dropbox.com). Sign up for an account there and use applications such as Scanner Pro (a scanning application), or text editor PlainText to save files there.

Apple's free iBooks app can also sync PDF files opened on your iPhone back to iTunes on your computer.

How can I make my battery last longer?

1 Quit some multitasking apps

Some streaming audio apps can continue to play in the background and therefore eat into your battery life. To stop them running completely, press the Home button twice to bring up the multitasking dock. Tap and hold the app icon to quit and tap the red badge that appears.

2 Lose the Wi-Fi

If you rarely use Wi-Fi, you can turn it off to save battery power. Go to Settings>Wi-Fi and set Wi-Fi to Off. Note that if you frequently use your iPhone to browse the web, battery life may be improved by using Wi-Fi instead of cellular data networks.

3 Turn off 3G

Using 3G cellular networks means faster data on the go, but it eats battery life in areas with limited 3G coverage. To disable 3G go to Settings>General >Network and set Enable 3G to Off. You can still make and receive calls and access cellular data networks.

5 Turn off your iPhone

When left on standby, your iPhone will use some battery power if it's checking for email, or receiving texts or calls. Unless you're likely to need to check your email in the middle of the night, turn your iPhone off when you go to bed, so you'll still have energy in the morning.

4 Lower the brightness

The iPhone's screen is one of its biggest power draws, so in the Settings slide the Brightness slider down to improve battery life. And turn off the Auto-Brightness setting, which adjusts the screen's brightness by monitoring its environment – again you'll save a few minutes of battery life this way.

"The iPhone's screen is one of its biggest power draws"

6 Don't notify me, thanks

The iPhone's Push Notification service lets certain apps alert you of new messages. But lots of notifications use up lots of power, so disable those you don't need. In Settings>Notifications, set Notifications to Off. Notifications for that app will now only be received when it is next launched.

7 Who needs an equalizer?

If you don't consider yourself much of an audiophile, the chances are that you won't be needing to adjust the iPod app's Equalizer. So why keep it activated, as applying it to songs can decrease your iPhone's battery life? Turning EQ off is incredibly simple, go to Settings>iPod>EQ and make sure it is set to Off.

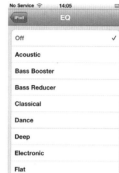

8 Make better email settings

Continual checking for email eats battery life. The longer the interval between checks, the longer your battery will last. So adjust your settings accordingly. Head over to Settings>Mail, Contacts, Calendars>Fetch New Data, choose to check for new email messages every hour – or even manually.

9 Do you need Location Services?

Location Services allows apps to identify your iPhone's location.

But why not just turn it on when you need it and save batteries? To disable it, go to Settings>General >Location Services and move the slider to 'Off'. When you need to know where you are, turn this setting back on.

10 Edit spotlight

The iPhone's Spotlight feature can be a handy way to find stray emails or apps, but its background indexing takes a minor toll on battery life. Reduce this under Settings> General>Spotlight Search and choose the type of items you're likely to need to search for and disable the rest.

Troubleshooting

What do I do when my iPhone freezes?

Generally speaking your iPhone is an incredibly reliable device. But sometimes – and for no accountable reason – weird things start to happen.

One of the more alarming issues is that the iPhone may suddenly freeze up and stop responding to touch or applications may refuse to quit.

There are a number of simple steps you can take to solve these problems, however. Many can be resolved by simply forcing an app to quit, while others may require a more in-depth restore. And it's also worth investigating whether other things may have triggered a freeze.

For example, if your iPhone refuses to turn on, it may be that a dead battery is at the root of the problem, rather than a software issue. If this is the case simply charge up your iPhone until it turns back on. And if you suffer from freezes on a regular basis, take the iPhone back to an Apple Store to make sure that a hardware problem isn't the cause.

But here are three simple ways to help you solve the freezing problems you may encounter from time to time.

> "If your iPhone refuses to turn on, it may be that a dead battery is at the root of the problem"

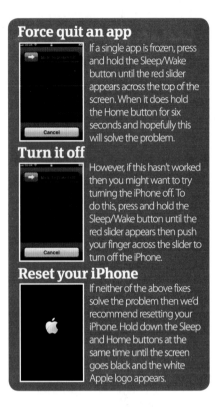

Force quit an app
If a single app is frozen, press and hold the Sleep/Wake button until the red slider appears across the top of the screen. When it does hold the Home button for six seconds and hopefully this will solve the problem.

Turn it off
However, if this hasn't worked then you might want to try turning the iPhone off. To do this, press and hold the Sleep/Wake button until the red slider appears then push your finger across the slider to turn off the iPhone.

Reset your iPhone
If neither of the above fixes solve the problem then we'd recommend resetting your iPhone. Hold down the Sleep and Home buttons at the same time until the screen goes black and the white Apple logo appears.

Can I reset the white balance on the Camera app?

Like any camera, the photos you take with your iPhone camera are affected by its surroundings. Those taken indoors have a different colour temperature to those taken outside, and this may lead to odd colour casts on your photos.

Most cameras have a function to correct white balance. While the iPhone's Camera app doesn't have this, it automatically adjusts settings, including brightness and white balance, when it focuses. So if your image is too light, you can adjust white balance by tapping your finger on a slightly darker part of the image, which will cause the camera to recalibrate all its settings.

> "iPhone's Camera will automatically adjust photo brightness"

What is jailbreaking?

Jailbreaking is basically a method that allows iPhone users to run any program on their device, rather than just those that have been officially approved by Apple.

Jailbreaking first became popular back in the iPhone's early days before Apple had even released its now iconic App Store. At that time, there was no way to add your own apps to the iPhone unless you circumvented Apple's rules, and the art of jailbreaking provided the answer to this problem.

The arrival of the App Store dampened enthusiasm for jailbreaking, but there are still reasons why some people might want to jailbreak their phone. In particular, jailbreaking allows you to customise your iPhone in ways currently not allowed by Apple. For example, you can extensively tailor your Home screen to remove text or add widgets.

Apple's strong guidelines on what is allowed in the App Store still grates on some users. Jailbreaking offers a more open approach to installing applications, with all the benefits and drawbacks that brings. In fact there's even a thriving App Store that makes it easy to browse and download apps for jailbroken phones. Among these are programs that allow you to perform actions not available to non-jailbroken iPhones; for example, switching Wi-Fi settings on and off quickly, adding more customisation to your Home screen and much more.

Three ways to view Flash

LogMeIn Ignition

A £20 purchase from the App Store, LogMeIn allows you to log into and control your computer from your iPhone as well as allowing you to watch Flash video.

And while you can view Flash video through LogMeIn, performance limitations will rule it out for normal use on all but the fastest connections. But where it earns its corn is if you're blocked out of a Flash-dependent website on your iPhone. Log into your computer using LogMeIn Ignition, and you can get at the content you need.

Skyfire

This app famously grabbed 300,000 users on its launch weekend, and then bizarrely claimed to be 'sold out'. It certainly grabbed the headlines – but beneath the hype, Skyfire is an iPhone web browser that can view a host of Flash content on the web. How does it manage this? By sending the Flash video to its own servers, which re-encode it in a format suitable for the iPhone. It's a roundabout way to get Flash on your iPhone, but in most situations it works fine.

Cloud Browse

Although it's only available on the US Apple Store, Cloud Browse is worth keeping an eye on, as its underlying premise is simple and will no doubt be copied elsewhere. Cloud Browse runs a desktop version of a standard Firefox browser on its servers and then streams that content direct to your iPhone screen when you enter the URL. Essentially you're running a Windows version on Firefox, with the Flash plug-in installed and the ability to run Java apps too. It's hardly sophisticated, but it does work.

Can you view Flash on your iPhone?

Adobe's Flash is a technology that makes it possible to embed video, games and multimedia content on websites. Its appeal to web developers is that it is quick to load thanks to small file sizes, and its cross-platform compatibility.

But Apple has refused to allow Flash anywhere near the iPhone. Apple points to what it claims is a history of instability on Macs – the company says that Flash is the number one cause of web browser crashes – to back up its view. Flash's reputation for being power-hungry could also, Apple argues, be a critical flaw on a device where battery life is so important.

Other smartphones do offer various versions of Flash, with mixed success. But Apple is pinning its hopes on alternative, open technologies, such as a new version of HTML, HTML5. It's still early days, but Apple can point to some success, with many sites now offering Flash-free alternatives for iPhone users.

But what if you're visiting one of those sites that insist on Flash? Despite the company's best efforts, there are ways of circumventing Apple's ban and viewing Flash content on your iPhone. At the top of the page we've listed the best.

"There are ways of avoiding Apple's ban and viewing Flash content on your iPhone"

Troubleshooting

How do you turn off in-app purchases?

With some iPhone applications, what you pay for is what you get. Others adopt a different approach, by offering the actual app for a lower charge – or free – and then including certain additional features at a cost. These extras can be bought from within the application and are called in-app purchases.

In-app purchases can cover all sorts of things, including additional game levels, extra features or as part of a subscription for a publication. In some cases, they are invaluable. The ability to buy an individual copy of the publication without having to leave the app is a real timesaver. With such subscriptions, you can even set purchases to automatically recur.

But on some occasions, in-app purchasing has proved controversial. With certain games, particularly those targeted at children, some parents allege that it has been too easy for kids to rack up large bills through in-app purchases.

While you do have to enter your iTunes password for in-app purchases, you're not prompted again for your password for 15 minutes after first entering it, allowing a spending window for kids. But you can make things even more secure by blocking them altogether.

Here's how to prevent in-app purchases from being made.

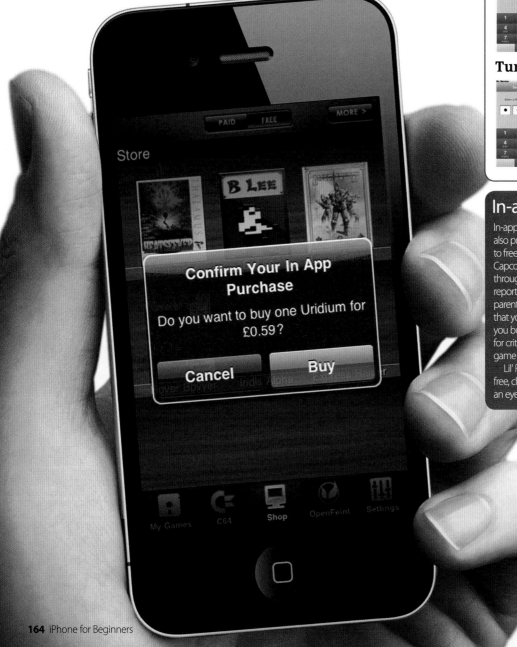

How to block in-app purchases

Enable restrictions

Fortunately, turning off in-app purchases is incredibly straightforward. Simply go to Settings>General. Tap Restrictions. When the next window pops up, tap on 'Enable Restrictions'.

Set a passcode

Enter a passcode, and then confirm it by re-entering it. You will need to enter this passcode every time you want to make any changes to your restrictions. Restrictions are now enabled for all of your apps.

Turn in-apps off

Leave all the other restriction options as they are, but under the 'Allowed Content' section, slide the 'In-App Purchase' slider into the Off position. No more in-app purchases will be allowed unless this setting is changed.

In-app controversy

In-app purchases may have their uses, but they have also proved controversial, particularly when it comes to free apps aimed at children. One developer, Capcom Mobile, has made a lot of money through in-app purchases of Smurf's Village, which reportedly received numerous complaints from parents about accidental purchases of 'smurfberries' that you use in the game. Tap Zoo, an app that lets you build and stock your own zoo, has also come in for criticism. Some elements that help success in the game can cost up to £12 each.

Lil' Pirates is another app that, while ostensibly free, charges for some features of the game: up to an eye-watering £60 for some game elements.

Press the switch

The first thing to do to turn off your iPhone is hold down the Sleep/Wake button in the top right-hand corner of your device until a red slider appears on your screen.

Slide to turn off

To turn the iPhone off, move your finger across the red slider. If you change your mind, simply press the Cancel button at the bottom and you'll be taken back to the Home screen.

Turning back on

Turning your iPhone back on is just as simple. Hold down the Sleep/Wake button until the Apple icon appears on the screen. In a few seconds your Home screen will appear.

Does the iPhone turn off or just go to sleep?

The iPhone has two inactive states: sleep and off. When you press your iPhone's Sleep/Wake button, it goes into Sleep mode, which turns off and locks the screen. It saves battery power, but still wakes up automatically to receive incoming calls or displays text messages as you receive them.

Your iPhone will also sleep when it's inactive. But sometimes it's better to shut down your iPhone completely. While a sleeping iPhone will still draw some power, a switched-off iPhone consumes almost none. If your battery is low, turning the phone off will save its energy as much as possible. There are a couple of disadvantages of turning the iPhone off. You won't receive calls or texts, and it takes a few seconds to turn back on again. Check out our tips on the left to learn how to turn it off.

"Sleep mode turns off and locks the screen and saves battery power"

Can you view PDFs on an iPhone?

Yes, you can. The iPhone has its own built-in PDF reader that lets you open PDFs and scroll and zoom through them. It's great for viewing email attachments.

But you can also open PDFs in other applications too, such as the inexpensive GoodReader, which handles large PDF files and even lets you add annotations and highlights to PDF pages or even iBooks, which will let you sync PDFs with iTunes. You can choose which app will open the PDF the first time you open it – buttons at the top of the PDF let you choose which one to use.

Can I take a screenshot of my iPhone?

A screenshot is simply a picture of your screen. But why might you want to take a screenshot? There are all sorts of reasons. For example, you might want to illustrate how to perform an action on an iPhone, share images of your favourite iPhone Home screens, grab a picture of a high-score screen on a game, or even take a still of a movie to use as your iPhone's wallpaper.

All these things are possible with screenshots, and yet the best thing about taking them is that it is superbly simple to do so. There's no need to install an extra app to take a screenshot – the functionality is built right into the iPhone. And there's no complicated method of managing them either. Once you've taken the screenshot you can send the resulting image by email or sync it with your computer in a matter of seconds.

Choose the shot

First off you'll need to navigate to the screen you want to take a screenshot of – it doesn't matter whether it's the iPhone's Home screen, a webpage, an app or a game.

Taking the screenshot

Holding down the 'Home' button, press down on the 'Sleep' button simultaneously. The iPhone will flash and make a camera shutter sound as it takes the screenshot.

Storing the shot

The screenshot is saved to the Camera Roll of your Camera app. From there you can email it or sync it to your computer as you would with other Camera Roll images.

"It's superbly simple to take a screenshot"

Can I replace the battery?

The iPhone's batteries are not designed to be replaceable. But don't worry: with normal use, they should last for several years.

If you find that your battery won't hold a charge, you can find replacement batteries online, although you'll require some dexterity with a soldering iron to fit it, and doing so will invalidate your warranty.

Troubleshooting

How do I delete things off my iPhone?

It's easy to get into the habit of collecting things that you never use on your iPhone. The App Store has a plethora of tempting apps to try out, and the superb camera on the iPhone is simply an invitation to take snapshots with abandon.

But it's all too easy to let things get cluttered. Unwanted apps can make the apps you want

much more difficult to find, while too many photos can be difficult to manage when you sync back to your computer.

But the biggest problem is the amount of space these unwanted apps and photos take up on the iPhone's hard drive. No matter how big the capacity of your iPhone, it's incredibly easy

to reach its ceiling, and there will come a point in time when you are desperate to get rid of some of this unwanted baggage.

Allied to this is the fact that backups – which take place every time you sync your iPhone to your PC or Mac – take a lot longer the more stuff you cram on your iPhone.

Delete apps

With so many free and inexpensive apps available on the App Store, it's tempting to run wild and install as many as you can. But in most cases, people only use a fraction of the apps they have installed on their phones, the others sit unused for months on end, demanding frequent updates, but offering little functional value. Why not dump the ones that you don't need?

Delete the icon

Deleting an app is incredibly easy to do. First of all you will need to tap and hold on the icon of the app you want to delete until all of the iPhone icons on your Home screen begin to wobble. Now tap on the 'X' icon in the top-left corner of the unwanted app's icon.

Confirm delete

Once you've clicked on the 'X' on the icon of the app you wish to delete a confirmation alert will pop up asking if you're sure you want to delete the app. If you wish to proceed press the Delete button to confirm or hit cancel if you'd rather keep the app after all.

Return to normal

Once you've got rid all of the apps you wanted to you'll want to stop all of the other icons from shaking around on your Home screen. To return your iPhone to its normal state, simply press the Home button once. The apps should then stop wiggling.

Delete photos

The iPhone makes it so easy to take pictures that you're likely to end up with far more than you want. And if you don't keep on top of your collection, the next time you sync these photos back to your computer, you'll end up with dozens of images clogging up your photo library.

The good news is that it's easy to delete images from your iPhone. Here's how to go about it.

Deleting single snapshots

In Camera app delete a photo you've just taken by tapping the icon at the bottom left of the screen to open the image, and then tapping the Trash icon.

Deleting multiple snaps

To delete more photos, tap the Camera Roll button, tap the arrow button at the bottom of the screen, so that Select Items appears in the Title.

Remove the photos

Tap on the photos that you want to delete – a small tick will appear over each one. Now press the Delete button to remove all of the selected photos.

> "The App Store has a host of tempting apps to try out, and the superb camera on the iPhone is simply an invitation to take snapshots with abandon"

Delete contacts

It's not that you've suddenly fallen out with all your friends, but there are a few reasons for occasionally filleting your contacts list. Perhaps the most obvious is also the most frequent: a failed sync can create doubles of contacts that can then get mixed up as you add details to one version of the contact but not the other.

Or perhaps you've synced contacts from numerous locations – you can sync from Yahoo! Address Book contacts and Google Contacts which again can add a host of extra unwanted contacts to your iPhone. Here's how to get rid of them.

Delete on the iPhone

Tap the name of the icon you want to delete. In the next window, tap Edit. Scroll down to the bottom of the contact and press Delete Contact.

Delete multiple contacts

You can't get rid of multiple contacts in the iPhone. To reset your contacts list, open iTunes, select your iPhone in the Devices list. Select the Info tab.

Reset your contacts

In 'Advanced', check the option next to contacts. During the next sync, iTunes will replace contacts on your iPhone with those on your computer.

Delete songs

There are plenty of reasons for deleting a song on your iPhone.

There's only one problem: without jailbreaking your iPhone you can't actually directly delete the songs on your iPhone. We presume this is a feature that's been included to protect any content you've bought on iTunes.

So you'll need to delete your music from iTunes and then sync it. It's a fairly simple process, and here's how to do it.

Start syncing

Check how iTunes is syncing. Select your iPhone in the Devices list. Under the Music tab, check whether it's syncing everything or just some playlists.

Delete from playlist

If it's syncing playlists, select that playlist in the source list and drag the offending track out of it. Now sync your iPhone (choose File >Sync).

Permanently delete track

If you're syncing all music, it's simpler to delete the track. Choose Edit> Delete and press Remove when prompted. Now sync your iPhone.

> "A large email database will take longer for Spotlight to search"

Delete emails

Emails are sometimes vital, sometimes trivial. In fact, they can be so varied that it would be pointless to store every single one. And in the case of those with large attachments that you've downloaded on your iPhone, could also eat up valuable disk space.

Another advantage of deleting emails that you don't want to keep is speed. A large email database takes longer for Spotlight to search. It's much easier to delete emails on your iPhone than it is on a desktop computer, it makes sense to learn how to do it. Here's how.

Deleting single emails

Select the email you wish to delete from your inbox and drag your finger over it to the right. A Delete button will then pop up, press it and the email will be moved to the Trash for that particular account.

Deleting multiple emails

If you want to delete a group of emails rather than one specific message you will need to tap the Edit button, then tap the buttons next to each email you would like to delete. Then hit the delete button to send them to the Trash.

Empty the Trash

As you will have noticed, both of the previous steps only put the email in the Trash. To fully delete your chosen messages, you will need to open the email account's Trash, and repeat the deletion there.

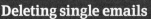

Troubleshooting

Why isn't my SIM card being recognised?

If the 'No SIM' message is displayed on your screen, the most likely cause is that the SIM card isn't placed properly in its tray, so try re-seating it. On the iPhone 4 you can access the tray by gently pushing the tip of a paper clip into the hole on the right-hand side of the phone.

The tray containing the SIM should pop out. Check the SIM card is correctly inserted and push the tray back in properly. The message should disappear. If this doesn't work, try another SIM card from the same provider. Otherwise, a trip to the Apple Store is in order.

How do you prevent the screen from scratching?

The iPhone 4's screen is much tougher than any previous model, but that doesn't mean it's totally resistant to scratching.

There's no sure-fire way of avoiding scratches on the phone's screen, but the most effective way to protect your screen is to keep it in a case, or cover it with a protective film.

But if you prefer to keep your iPhone 4 naked, take a common-sense approach to the screen's upkeep. Keep it away from hard items that are likely to scratch it, such as keys and coins. That way, your screen will still look unblemished for months to come.

Does Skype work on the iPhone?

Skype is a well-known service that has grown from a utility offering free calls to other Skype users, as well as cheap calls to other landline and mobile phones to something much bigger.

Now boasting around 700 million registered accounts worldwide, Skype, the largest international voice carrier, also lets you video chat and text with Skype contacts. Its iPhone app offers all these features and as its video chats work over a 3G network as well as Wi-Fi, it has an advantage over FaceTime in this respect.

Most people will use Skype to call others, and here it's a fantastic tool to use. As an iPhone user, you're either paying a monthly charge for calls and texts, or perhaps even paying for each individual call. Install Skype on your iPhone – and those of your friends and family – and you can switch to a cheaper tariff or avoid call charges altogether.

Because Skype supports multitasking it can run in the background on more recent iPhones. That means you can receive Skype calls and messages while another app is running in the foreground.

The only caveat to be aware of is bandwidth. Video calling in particular is demanding – it uses a little under 4Mb of data a minute, so you may well eat into your phone provider's data limits if you're not careful.

Skype isn't the only app you can use to make free calls to your friends. There are plenty of rivals, including Viber, which allows free high-quality calls to other Viber users anywhere in the world, and Fring, which, like Skype, also offers video-calling as well as audio – and its even planning a group video chat feature. A future update will eventually allow users to chat with up to four participants on screen at once.

While many of these solutions are available on both iPhone and Android, they require the person you're calling to have the application on their iPhone or computer. As long as you're calling another iPhone user, your best bet might be FaceTime, which comes with all recent iPhones, iPod touches and iPads, and is even available on the Mac.

"Video calling is demanding – it uses a little under 4Mb of data a minute"

Get to grips with Skype on iPhone

Login to Skype

Launch Skype and enter your password. You'll need to set up an account if you don't have one. You're taken to the Contacts screen – contacts already created on a desktop version of Skype are seen here.

Contact your contacts

Tap the contact's name to open their screen, where you can call, video chat or send a message. Tapping the Call button on the navigation bar lets you dial a number using a keypad.

Check your details

Tap the My Info button in the navigation bar to open the screen showing how much credit you have left (tap on it to add more), or turn on voice forwarding or activate Voicemail.

The Wi-Fi connection

You can tell if you're connected to a Wi-Fi network easily. At the top of your screen you should see the Wi-Fi icon, and the boldness of the bars indicate the strength of your reception.

Check the listing

If you lose your Wi-Fi connection, tap Settings > Wi-Fi and tap the arrow to see whether your Wi-Fi network is available. It will appear on a list of networks if you are still in range.

Jump-starting things

If you can see your network, but can't connect, go to Settings > Wi-Fi and turn Wi-Fi off and then turn it back on again. However, if that doesn't work, turn your iPhone off, then on again.

I can't seem to connect to Wi-Fi?

Your iPhone has the built-in ability to surf the net and send emails over the phone network. But you can also use Wi-Fi which has its advantages. Transferring data over Wi-Fi is faster than 3G, and is unencumbered by the data restrictions imposed by phone providers.

Your iPhone should automatically offer Wi-Fi in preference to 3G when it's within range of a Wi-Fi connection. The only problem is that sometimes your iPhone won't see the Wi-Fi connection or will drop it for no apparent reason.

If you're having trouble finding a decent Wi-Fi connection, there are a couple of things you can do. First, take care of the obvious stuff. Make sure your Wi-Fi router is turned on and is working properly – one way to do this is to check other devices (for example, your computer) can pick up the Wi-Fi connection and access the internet. Then try our tips on the left.

"Your iPhone should automatically offer Wi-Fi in preference to 3G when it's within range of a Wi-Fi connection"

Can I unlock my iPhone if I forget my passcode?

Putting a passcode on your iPhone is, for the most part, an excellent idea. The four-figure combination lock not only prevents prying eyes viewing the important documents on your iPhone should you leave it lying around somewhere, but it also provides a modest deterrent against stealing your iPhone in the first place.

But sometimes your well-intentioned security will backfire on you, and it's human error that may be the cause. If you forget the password, for obvious reasons there's no easy way to recover it. Your iPhone will generously give you a few attempts to enter your passcode correctly, but will then lock you out for increasingly longer periods.

On the point of giving up? Don't worry. Even if you're locked out you can restore your iPhone from an existing backup on iTunes. This will remove the password protection on your iPhone, although you will also lose any saved passwords on your apps, too.

Restore your iPhone

With the iPhone attached to your computer running iTunes, hold the Home and Sleep/Wake buttons down for ten seconds and then release the Sleep button. Keep holding the Home button down.

Recovery mode

Your iPhone displays an icon telling you to connect to iTunes, while iTunes will tell you when it has detected an iPhone in recovery mode. Now press the Restore button in iTunes.

Resetting the password

It may take some time to restore your iPhone. But once it's ready, you can reset your password under Settings> General>Passcode Lock. Just make sure you don't forget it this time!

Troubleshooting

I'm having trouble syncing my iPhone

There's little more annoying than a failed sync. Here's how to avoid frustration

If you're having problems syncing your iPhone to iTunes, it's a serious issue.

After all, syncing with iTunes is an indispensable part of using your iPhone. Not only does syncing make sure that the content on your iPhone matches what you might have downloaded on your computer (and vice versa), but every time you sync, iTunes also backs up your iPhone, so if

you subsequently encounter a serious problem with your phone, the worst-case scenario is that you'll be able to restore from a previous backup.

So when you encounter a problem with syncing, don't ignore the issue. Syncing problems, while rare, can be varied. They range from iTunes not recognising your iPhone at all, through slow sync errors, to iTunes not backing up at all, or

syncs failing for no apparent reason, with obscure error messages not providing a great deal of help.

While all these errors can be alarming, the best approach is to deal with them calmly. Step through the issue to localise the problem if you can, and address it from there.

Here are some common iTunes sync errors, with some advice on how to deal with them.

---

iPhone doesn't appear in iTunes

You connect your iPhone to your computer, launch iTunes, and naturally expect your iPhone to start syncing. But what if it doesn't? In fact what if not only does the sync not take place, but your iPhone doesn't even appear in the left column of iTunes under the Devices list. It's a fairly fundamental problem, but here's some steps you can take that should help you to rectify matters and spark the iPhone back to life.

Can't see your iPhone?

There are a few things you can do if your iPhone isn't displaying in iTunes. The first thing to do is make sure you're running the latest version of your operating system and the latest version of iTunes. Open iTunes, then choose iTunes > Check for Updates.

Recharge your iPhone

As with many other potential iPhone issues the problem may be that your phone isn't fully charged and that's why it isn't appearing in the Devices list. Leave it attached for a few minutes to charge sufficiently and then it should automatically appear once it has some power

Restart your iPhone

If none of the previous steps have worked you'll want to try turning your phone off and back on again. Turn your iPhone off by holding down the Sleep/Wake button until the red slider appears. Slide to turn off. Restart by holding down the Sleep/Wake button.

Backup takes too long

iTunes will automatically back up your iPhone every time you sync it to your computer. But a slow backup can mean that you're waiting for ages for the iPhone to back up even before you start syncing all of your content – and that means your iPhone may be out of action for a

good few minutes while it waits to sync media you have recently downloaded from the App Store or iTunes. From software errors and lack of space on your iPhone to corrupt apps, there are dozens of potential causes of this problem, but here are a couple of things to do to speed things up.

Diagnose the problem

There could be plenty of reasons for slow backups: corrupt apps, or a software error. But if your iPhone is syncing for too long try deleting some media.

Transfer photos

Having a lot of photos on your iPhone's Camera Roll can really slow backups down. Transfer them to your computer, and delete them on the iPhone.

Remove apps

Having dozens of apps can also slow down a backup. Use iTunes to pare down the number of apps on your iPhone. The same goes for audio tracks, too.

Can't sync my favourite podcast

Even if your iPhone connects and backs up properly, what happens if your favourite tracks just won't transfer over from iTunes to your iPhone? No clear explanation is given: you just get a strange error message saying that your iPhone can't be synced because an unknown error occurred. In this case, the error given is (13019), but trying again just produces the same message. What can you do to solve it?

"What happens if your favourite tracks won't transfer over to your iPhone?"

The error message

The symptom of the problem is that when you try to sync you get a strange error message that tells you that an error occurred. What to do?

Deselect Voice Memos

In iTunes, select your iPhone under devices. Click the Music tab and under the 'Sync music' option, deselect the Voice Memos playlist.

An alternative solution

Deselect the Sync Music option under the Music tab. Click Apply and then Sync. Once synced, reselect the Sync Music option and click Apply.

Not enough space to sync

If there's one problem with syncing that is likely to come to all of us at some point, it is a lack of space on your iPhone.

You're happily syncing the content between your computer and your iPhone, when suddenly it grinds to a halt, complaining that there isn't enough free space left on your iPhone.

The problem, then, is fairly obvious, but just how do you go about solving it? Here's the simple way to define the problem and address it.

What's causing the problem?

The bar at the bottom of the iTunes window shows how much space each media type is taking up. Here, video is the problem.

Understanding the error

You've tried to sync, but you get an error message saying you're over capacity. Clear enough, but how do you solve it?

Deleting the content

There's too much video content being synced. Click on the Video tab and deselect the videos. The bar updates at the bottom as you deselect items.

Error syncing pictures

Even though they're the most common, it's not only music and apps that are synced between your computer and iPhone. Pictures are too, and occasionally you can run into syncing problems here as well.

One of the more common picture-related problems occurs when trying to sync and you get the following error message:

"The iPhone cannot be synced. An unknown error occurred (-39)." Here are some steps you can take to address this particular problem.

Deselect the images

With your iPhone connected to iTunes, select it under Devices and select the Pictures tab. Uncheck all the image events and albums. Click Apply.

Reselect the images

Now go back and reselect those images that you deselected in the previous step. Click the Apply button. This should solve the problem.

An alternative solution

On a Mac you can get the same effect by simply right-clicking the Pictures>iPhoto Library folder and selecting 'Show Package Contents'. Select the 'iPod Photo cache' and delete.

"You can run into problems when syncing pictures to the iPhone"

Troubleshooting

How do you register an iTunes gift card?

iTunes gift cards are prepaid cards that can be used to buy music, download films or purchase apps from the iTunes Store.

But what's the appeal of the gift card, if you can just buy content from iTunes as and when you need it? The obvious reason is that it makes a great present for those with an iPhone and for both the security conscious and for children, a gift card removes the need for a credit card.

Gift cards work very simply. It should only take a few seconds for you to redeem the code on the back of the card on the iTunes Store. You're instantly allocated credit corresponding to the value of the gift card. Every time you subsequently buy an item from the iTunes Store, the value of that transaction will be taken from the card's credit balance, until it's completely depleted. You'll always be able to see the amount of available credit so you know how much you have spare.

Above we've shown instructions for redeeming a gift card on the iTunes Store on your iPhone, but you can also redeem a gift from the App Store app, too – or even iTunes on your PC or Mac.

> "It should only take a few seconds for you to redeem the code"

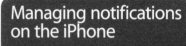

What are push notifications?

Back when apps for the iPhone first arrived, users of popular text messaging apps discovered a fundamental problem. When you quit the app, you weren't able to receive messages from others.

Apple's way of combating issues like this is the Push Notifications service, which allows apps on your iPhone to send you messages or updates even when the application isn't running.

Notifications can take many forms – they can display text alerts on screen, offer an audio warning, or even attach a badge to the app's icon. Their availability depends on the application. You'll find that many apps that involve communication with others, such as Twitter and Facebook, have this functionality built in.

With push notification technology open to any app that wants to use it, the risk is that you'll be overwhelmed with messages and alerts that you might not actually want.

And given that push notifications can have a mild impact on battery life – even when your iPhone is asleep, it will check every 15 minutes for a notification – you want to be able to choose which applications update you.

Fortunately Apple has thought of this and allows you to configure which apps can send push notifications. Here's how to set it up.

> "Push notifications can have a mild impact on battery life so you'll want to be able to choose which apps update you"

Managing notifications on the iPhone

Open iTunes app

When you install an app with push notifications you're asked when you launch it to choose whether or not to allow them. If you change your mind, you can manage them in Settings.

Manage notifications

Open Settings> Notifications. Slide the top bar to Off to turn off all notifications. But if you turn them on, you can set notifications for individual apps. Each app with notifications is listed below.

Control individual apps

Underneath the app's name you can see whether notifications are turned on for it. Tap the app's name and you can control how you want to be notified by that app – either Sounds, Alerts or Badges.

Does FaceTime only work with other iPhones?

No, it's much more flexible. FaceTime will also allow video chatting with owners of the latest generation of iPod touches (4th generation) and iPads, as well as Mac users who have the Mac's FaceTime application installed.

The only difference when FaceTime calling someone on those devices is that instead of using an iPhone number to call them – as you would do when using FaceTime between iPhones – you use the email address that they have designated as their FaceTime address.

As long as they are connected to a Wi-Fi network you should be able to video chat with them.

How do you tell how much space is left on your iPhone?

Finding out how much space you have left on your iPhone isn't difficult. When you connect your iPhone to your Mac or PC, iTunes will give you get an instant overview of your iPhone's available capacity.

Simply click on your iPhone in the sidebar (under the 'Devices' heading), and under the Summary tab you will see a graphical overview of what is taking up space on your phone. The amount of space taken up by the likes of apps, music, videos, podcasts and ringtones will all be displayed.

However, you don't have to log in to iTunes to find out how much free space you have, you can also work out your free space directly on your iPhone. Tap Settings and under General, click 'About'. Next to the 'Available' heading you will see how much space you have left on your device.

Go creative with Mac, iPad & iPh

Upskill today with the very best creative bookazines and DVDs

Mac for Beginners vol 3
Starting with the basics, this essential guide will teach you how to get to grips with every aspect of your Mac, from iLife and iWork to iTunes, Safari and Mail.
SRP: £12.99

iPhone Tips, Tricks, Apps & Hacks vol 4
Step-by-step tutorials and features covering the secrets of the iPhone and a jailbreaking guide make this a must-own.
SRP: £9.99

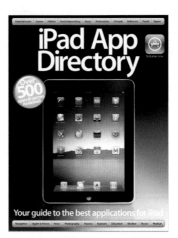

iPad App Directory vol 1
Save yourself time and money by using our definitive guide to the best apps on the App Store. Every category is covered and there are over 500 apps reviewed inside.
SRP: £9.99

iPhone App Directory vol 7
The world's best iPhone applications are reviewed right here, including the very best for iPhone 4, with every App Store category featured inside.
SRP: £9.99

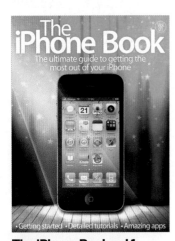

The iPhone Book vol 1
Whether you're brand new to the iPhone or have had one for a while, this book is the ultimate resource for getting the best from your favourite device.
SRP: £9.99

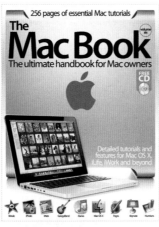

The Mac Book vol 6
256 pages of practical and creative tutorials and in-depth features that will take you through OS X, iLife, iWork and even third-party applications.
SRP: £12.99

iPhone Games Directory vol 2
The world's most comprehensive guide to iPhone, iPod touch and iPad gaming apps, with all gaming genres reviewed and rated.
SRP: £9.99

iLife Genius Guide vol 2
Easy-to-follow 256-page tutorial guide to the complete suite of Apple iLife apps including iPhoto, iMovie, iDVD, iWeb and GarageBand.
SRP: £12.99

your one

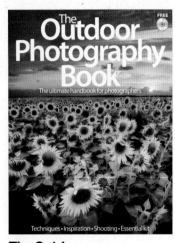

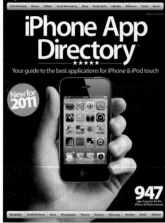

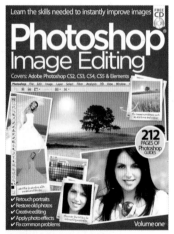

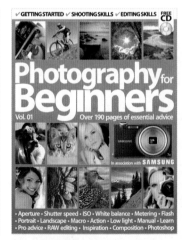